Vocabulary Workshop

The classic program for:

- *developing* and *enhancing* vocabulary resources

- *promoting* more effective communication in today's world

- *improving* vocabulary skills assessed on standardized and/or college-admission tests

By
Jerome Shostak

Sadlier-Oxford

A Division of William H. Sadlier, Inc.
New York
Chicago
Los Angeles

Copyright © 1988 by
Oxford Book Company, Inc.
A Division of
William H. Sadlier, Inc.

ISBN-0-87105-175-3
123456789/987

Home Office: 11 Park Place,
New York, NY 10007

For more than four decades,

VOCABULARY WORKSHOP has proved a highly effective tool for guiding and stimulating systematic vocabulary growth. In the *Expanded Edition,* every effort has been made to bolster and enhance the features that have made the series so successful, while preserving the format, organization, and scope of the original program. These features include:

Word List	Each book contains 300 or more basic words, carefully selected on the basis of: • currency in present-day usage • frequency on recognized vocabulary lists *New!* • current grade-placement research *New!* 10% of the list has been entirely revised.
Units	The words in each book are organized around 15 short but stimulating *Units* featuring: • pronunciation and part of speech • definition and illustrative phrase • sentences illustrating literal *and* figurative word usage *New!* • expanded treatment of synonyms and antonyms
Reviews	Five *Reviews* highlight and reinforce the work of the units through challenging exercises involving: *New!* • spelling • analogies • synonyms • word families • antonyms • sentence completions *New!* fuller treatment of analogies and two-word completions
Cumulative Reviews	Four *Cumulative Reviews* utilize standardized testing techniques to provide ongoing assessment of word mastery. *New!* • analogies • antonyms • two-word completions
Additional Features	▪ *Diagnostic Test* provides ready assessment of student needs at the outset of the term. ▪ *Vocabulary of Vocabulary* reviews terms and concepts needed for effective word study. *New!* • denotation/connotation, literal/figurative *New!* • context clues ▪ *Final Mastery Test* provides end-of-term assessment of student achievement. ▪ *Building with Word Roots* introduces the study of etymology.
Ancillary Materials	▪ The *Supplementary Testing Program* provides separate testing materials for each student text. *New!* • Unit Tests *New!* • greater variety in question types ▪ The *Teacher's Guide/Answer Key* supplies answers to all materials in the student text and testing program, as well as a thorough guide to the use of the series.

Over the years, VOCABULARY WORKSHOP has proved invaluable for preparing students to take the types of standardized vocabulary tests commonly used to assess grade placement, competence for graduation, and/or college readiness. Both author and publisher firmly believe that the *Expanded Edition* greatly enhances the value of the series in this regard.

Pronunciation Key

The pronunciation is indicated for every basic word introduced in this book. The symbols used for this purpose, as listed below, are similar to those appearing in most standard dictionaries of recent vintage. The author has consulted a large number of dictionaries for this purpose but has relied primarily on *Webster's Third New International Dictionary* and *The Random House Dictionary of the English Language (Unabridged).*

There are, of course, many English words for which two (or more) pronunciations are commonly accepted. In virtually all cases where such words occur in this book, the author has sought to make things easier for the student by giving just one pronunciation. The only significant exception occurs when the pronunciation changes in accordance with a shift in the part of speech. Thus we would indicate that *project* in the verb form is pronounced prə 'jekt, and in the noun form, 'präj ekt.

It is believed that these relatively simple pronunciation guides will be readily usable by the student. It should be emphasized, however, that the *best* way to learn the pronunciation of a word is to listen to and imitate an educated speaker.

Vowels	ā	lake	e	stress	ü	loot, new
	a	mat	ī	kni*fe*	u̇	foot, pull
	â	care	i	si*t*	ə	ru*g*, broken
	ä	bark, bottle	ō	flow	ər	bird, better
	au̇	doubt	ô	all, cord		
	ē	beat, word*y*	oi	o*il*		

Consonants	ch	*ch*ild, lecture	s	*c*ellar	wh	*wh*at
	g	*g*ive	sh	*sh*un	y	*y*earn
	j	*g*entle, bri*dg*e	th	*th*ank	z	i*s*
	ŋ	si*ng*	t̶h̶	*th*ose	zh	mea*s*ure

All other consonants are sounded as in the alphabet.

Stress	The accent mark *precedes* the syllable receiving the major stress: en 'rich

Parts of Speech	*adj.*	adjective	*int.*	interjection	*prep.*	preposition
	adv.	adverb	*n.*	noun	*v.*	verb
			part.	participle		
			pl.	plural		

The Vocabulary of Vocabulary

There are some interesting and useful words which are employed to describe and identify words. The exercises that follow will help you to check and strengthen your knowledge of the "vocabulary of vocabulary."

Synonyms and Antonyms

Synonyms

A *synonym* is a word that is similar in meaning to another word.

EXAMPLES:

eat—consume	clash—conflict
hurt—injure	fire—discharge

Exercises

In each of the following groups, encircle the word that is most nearly the **synonym** of the first word in **boldface type.**

1. amuse
a. delight
b. fancy
c. clear
d. deport

2. abundant
a. healthy
b. distant
c. ample
d. clever

3. hidden
a. conquered
b. hated
c. admired
d. concealed

4. craftsman
a. native
b. motorist
c. skilled worker
d. employee

5. melody
a. bar
b. staff
c. violin
d. tune

6. neat
a. sloppy
b. dull
c. tidy
d. overworked

7. continue
a. halt
b. inspect
c. condemn
d. endure

8. influence
a. position
b. money
c. education
d. effect

Antonyms

An *antonym* is a word that is opposite in meaning to another word.

EXAMPLES:

enter—leave	happy—miserable
wild—tame	leader—follower

Exercises

In each of the following groups, encircle the word that is most nearly the **antonym** of the first word in **boldface type.**

1. apparent
a. chance
b. risky
c. concealed
d. clear

2. feast
a. order
b. banquet
c. recipe
d. fast

3. fiction
a. ideal
b. truth
c. novel
d. notion

4. fix
a. trouble
b. please
c. change
d. break

5. honest
a. profitable
b. deceitful
c. gentle
d. loud

6. curious
a. odd
b. uninterested
c. neat
d. careful

7. difficult
a. easy
b. forceful
c. stubborn
d. boring

8. visible
a. concerned
b. content
c. possible
d. hidden

Words Pronounced Alike;
Words Spelled Alike

Homonyms

A *homonym* is a word having the same pronunciation as another word but a different meaning and a different spelling.

EXAMPLES:

know—no   pale—pail
horse—hoarse   flee—flea

Exercises

*In each of the following sentences, encircle in the parentheses the **homonym** that correctly completes the meaning.*

1. The judge (**fined, find**) the owner of the dog for allowing it to be in the streets without a leash.

2. To me the most beautiful of all (**flowers, flours**) is the early June rose.

3. I felt very uncomfortable being the (**lone, loan**) passenger on the bus.

4. I plan to (**where, wear**) my new outfit to school tomorrow.

5. I still do not know whether it was the (**rite, right, write**) thing to have done.

6. He placed the gift in a (**plane, plain**) box.

7. I watched the aircraft (**soar, sore**) out of sight.

8. I felt as though everyone in the theater was (**staring, stairing**) at me.

9. I think I have (**pored, poured**) some salt into the sugar bowl!

10. It costs more than I could (**urn, earn**) in a month.

Homographs

A *homograph* is a word that has the same spelling as another word but a different meaning.

EXAMPLES:

Spell may mean to indicate the letters of a word.
Spell may mean a charm or incantation.
Spell may mean an interval of rest or inactivity.

Most homographs, like those above, are not only spelled alike but pronounced alike. There are some, however, that are pronounced differently.

EXAMPLES:

Close, meaning to shut, is pronounced *klōz*.
Close, meaning nearby, is pronounced *klōs*.

Tear, meaning to rip, is pronounced *târ*.
Tear, meaning a drop of salty water from the eye, is pronounced *tēr*.

Homographs that are pronounced differently are sometimes called *heteronyms*.

Exercises	In Column C, write the homograph suggested by the definitions given in Columns A and B. The initial letter of the required word is given and the dashes represent the missing letters.

Column A	*Column B*	*Column C*
1. to declare	country	s _ _ _ _
2. to wear out	outer layer on wheel	t _ _ _
3. Chinese boat	worthless material	j _ _ _
4. place of trial	to woo	c _ _ _ _
5. large basket	to hinder	h _ _ _ _ _

Parts of a Word

Prefixes	A *prefix* is a syllable or syllables placed at the beginning of a word.
EXAMPLES:	*ex- dis- ab- per- in-*
Suffixes	A *suffix* is a syllable or syllables placed at the end of a word.
EXAMPLES:	*-ant -ence -or -ation*
Bases	A *base* or *root* is the main part of the word to which prefixes and suffixes may be added.
EXAMPLES:	*-fact- -pend- -sist-*
	Combining the prefix *in-* with the base *-sist-* and the suffix *-ence* gives us the word *insistence*.
NOTE:	The term *affix* may be used to designate either a prefix or a suffix. An affix is any addition to the base or root of a word.

Exercises	Divide each of the following words into its prefix, root, and suffix. Some of the words do not have either a prefix or a suffix. The first word has been done for you.

Word	*Prefix*	*Root*	*Suffix*
1. compartment	**com**	**part**	**ment**
2. resented	_____	_____	_____
3. enacting	_____	_____	_____
4. interruption	_____	_____	_____
5. diction	_____	_____	_____
6. addict	_____	_____	_____
7. recently	_____	_____	_____
8. complicate	_____	_____	_____
9. helpless	_____	_____	_____
10. referral	_____	_____	_____

Denotation and Connotation

Denotation   The denotation of a word is its specific dictionary meaning.

Examples:

Word	Denotation
eminent	noteworthy or distinguished
cumbersome	hard to handle or manage
remember	call to mind

Connotation   The *connotation* of a word is its tone—that is, the emotions or associations it normally arouses in people using, hearing, or reading it. Depending on what these feelings are, the connotation of a word may be *favorable (positive)* or *unfavorable (pejorative)*. A word that does not normally arouse strong feelings of any kind has a *neutral* connotation.

Examples:

Word	Connotation
eminent	favorable
cumbersome	unfavorable
remember	neutral

Exercises   *In the space provided, label the connotation of each of the following words* **F** *for "favorable,"* **U** *for "unfavorable," or* **N** *for "neutral."*

_____ **1.** mediocre   _____ **5.** reek   _____ **9.** plan

_____ **2.** article   _____ **6.** intrepid   _____ **10.** liberality

_____ **3.** drudgery   _____ **7.** sudden   _____ **11.** render

_____ **4.** enlightened   _____ **8.** clique   _____ **12.** illustrious

Literal and Figurative Usage

Literal Usage   When a word is used in a *literal* sense, it is being employed in its strict (or primary) dictionary meaning in a situation (or *context*) that "makes sense" from a purely logical point of view.

Example: Yesterday I read an old tale about a knight who slew a *fire-breathing* dragon.

Figurative Usage   Sometimes words are used in a symbolic or nonliteral way in situations that do not "make sense" from a purely logical point of view. We call this nonliteral or "extended" application of a word a *figurative* or *metaphorical* usage.

Example: Suddenly my boss rushed into my office *breathing fire*.

Exercises   *In the space provided, write* **L** *for "literal" or* **F** *for "figurative" next to each of the following sentences to show how the italicized expression is being used.*

_____ **1.** Tom *danced* with Sally at the prom.

_____ **2.** All kinds of delightful images *dance* across the pages of that novel.

_____ **3.** When I saw how popular he was with my friends, I turned *green* with envy.

_____ **4.** Last year I bought a new *green* pickup truck.

_____ **5.** It takes a *green* young rookie years to become a seasoned, streetwise veteran.

_____ **6.** The corn was not harvested while it was still *green*.

_____ **7.** As long as we don't have the funds to produce this project, it will have to stay *on the back burner*.

_____ **8.** I left the stew simmering *on the back burner* for several hours.

Analogies

An *analogy* is a comparison. For example, we can draw an analogy, or comparison, between a bird and an airplane.

In an examination, you will be asked to show that you know the meanings of words, and that you can think clearly, by recognizing an analogy between two different pairs. In the most common form of analogy question, two words are given that have a certain relationship. Then you are to select another pair of words having the same relationship.

EXAMPLE:

count is to **calculate** as
a. expand is to contract
b. plead is to annoy
c. turn is to twist
d. tire is to refresh

The relationship between the given pair of words, *calculate* and *count*, is that they are roughly *the same* in meaning. Look at the four other pairs of words. Which of them are most nearly synonyms? The answer clearly is (c) "turn is to twist," because *turn* and *twist*, have the same essential meaning.

Exercises

In each of the following, encircle the item that best completes the analogy.

1. peculiar is to **usual** as
a. loud is to musical
b. odd is to ordinary
c. wrong is to incorrect
d. angry is to mad

2. one is to **many** as
a. last is to most
b. cost is to price
c. soldier is to regiment
d. copy is to original

3. increase is to **heighten** as
a. crease is to fold
b. exclude is to include
c. lower is to involve
d. fear is to greet

4. donate is to **accept** as
a. remember is to recall
b. serve is to pay
c. perceive is to notice
d. give is to take

5. clear is to **cloudy** as
a. timid is to fearful
b. small is to tiny
c. bright is to dark
d. fine is to expensive

6. lucky is to **unfortunate** as
a. distant is to far
b. lost is to misplaced
c. found is to lost
d. tired is to weak

7. penniless is to **wealthy** as
a. strong is to muscular
b. dry is to arid
c. cowardly is to brave
d. hungry is to sleepy

8. pear is to **fruit** as
a. apple is to animal
b. cat is to mineral
c. sun is to element
d. pea is to vegetable

9. degree is to **temperature** as
a. pound is to weight
b. ruler is to length
c. ounce is to distance
d. foot is to capacity

10. shed is to **mansion** as
a. office is to mayor
b. eraser is to pencil
c. horse is to deer
d. bicycle is to automobile

Context Clues

When you do the various word-omission exercises in this book, look for *context clues* built into the passage to guide you to the correct answer.

Restatement Clues

A *restatement clue* consists of a synonym for, or a definition of, a missing word.

Example:

"I'm willing to <u>tell</u> you what I know about the matter," the reporter said, "but I can't _____ my sources."

a. conceal   b. defend   c. prosecute   (d.) reveal

Contrast Clues

A *contrast clue* consists of an antonym for, or a phrase that means the opposite of, a missing word.

Example:

"I'm trying to <u>help</u> you, <u>not</u> (**assist,** (**hinder**)) you!" I exclaimed in annoyance.

Inference Clues

An *inference clue* implies but does not directly state the meaning of a missing word.

Example:

A <u>utility infielder</u> has to be a very _____ player because he is a veritable "<u>jack-of-all-trades</u>" on the _____ diamond.

a. veteran . . . football   c. experienced . . . hockey
(b.) versatile . . . baseball   d. energetic . . . golf

Exercises   *Use context clues to choose the word or words that complete each of the following sentences or sets of sentences.*

1. Jonathan Swift once said that he didn't like people as a group but that he could put up with them _____ .

a. collectively   b. mechanically   c. individually   d. compactly

2. "Don't take the _____ off the line yet," mom told me as I searched around for the clothespin bag. "It is still _____ to the touch."

a. laundry . . . damp
b. telephone . . . dull
c. wash . . . dry
d. clothes . . . dirty

3. If you will supply the dishes for the picnic, I will (**furnish, eat**) the food.

Diagnostic Test

This test contains a sampling of the words that are to be found in the exercises in this Vocabulary Workshop. It will give you an idea of the types and levels of the words to be studied. When you have completed all the units, the Final Mastery Test at the end of this book will assess what you have learned. By comparing your results on the Final Mastery Test with your results on the Diagnostic Test below, you will be able to judge your progress.

Synonyms   In each of the following groups, encircle the word or phrase that most nearly expresses the meaning of the word in **boldface type** in the introductory phrase.

1. an **unkempt** appearance
   a. sudden   b. untidy   c. necessary   d. voluntary

2. chemicals that **adulterate** the food
   a. consume   b. pollute   c. purify   d. color

3. part of an **insidious** plan
   a. treacherous   b. recent   c. awkward   d. logical

4. the **belligerent** nations
   a. neighborly   b. wealthy   c. hostile   d. poor

5. lost in the **holocaust**
   a. confusion   b. struggle   c. results   d. great fire

6. an **adroit** driver
   a. careful   b. experienced   c. skillful   d. careless

7. a **cursory** examination
   a. hasty   b. thorough   c. very painful   d. rewarding

8. **delete** a portion of the selection
   a. read   b. cross out   c. emphasize   d. misunderstand

9. a clever **artifice**
   a. worker   b. reaction   c. statement   d. trick

10. seek **redress**
    a. health   b. remedy   c. costume   d. custom

11. **scrupulous** attention to details
    a. expert   b. careful   c. slight   d. childish

12. offer as a **panacea**
    a. cure-all   b. substitute   c. moneymaker   d. token

13. **cogent** reasoning
    a. false   b. organized   c. dulled   d. forceful

14. **altruistic** motives
    a. unselfish   b. complex   c. obvious   d. inner

15. **embark** at once
    a. cut   b. notice   c. cover   d. board

16. plead for **clemency**
a. justice   b. mercy   c. understanding   d. release

17. **accede** to their requests
a. listen   b. consent   c. deny   d. alter

18. an **officious** guard
a. efficient   b. hired   c. powerful   d. meddlesome

19. a **musty** closet
a. large   b. concealed   c. smelly   d. locked

20. an **endemic** species
a. interesting   b. native   c. peculiar   d. valuable

21. **reprehensible** behavior
a. worthy   b. blameworthy   c. criminal   d. remarkable

22. **turbulent** days
a. violent   b. fast   c. rainy   d. muddy

23. no longer **extant**
a. in existence   b. happy   c. in prison   d. visible

24. a **compatible** couple
a. married   b. divorced   c. agreeing   d. elderly

25. **deride** our efforts
a. compliment   b. mock   c. defend   d. extend

26. a **stentorian** voice
a. loud   b. grating   c. high   d. hushed

27. **gnarled** tree trunks
a. damaged   b. cut   c. knotty   d. tall

28. a **poignant** scene
a. humorous   b. moving   c. tiresome   d. noisy

29. **copious** notes
a. scribbled   b. clever   c. imitative   d. plentiful

30. unable to **acquiesce**
a. go along with   b. leave   c. obtain   d. understand

Antonyms *In each of the following groups, encircle the word or expression that is most nearly **opposite** in meaning to the word in **boldface type** in the introductory phrase.*

31. a worthy **adversary**
a. undertaking   b. opponent   c. ally   d. cause

32. a **dearth** of ideas
a. lack   b. association   c. source   d. abundance

33. **venal** arrangements
a. workable   b. honorable   c. corrupt   d. helpful

34. an overly **indulgent** parent
a. energetic   b. unconcerned   c. strict   d. confident

35. a **callous** attitude
a. sensitive   b. hostile   c. surprising   d. distant

36. a **quiescent** volcano
a. dormant   b. imposing   c. active   d. small

37. a **loquacious** person
a. tight-lipped   b. openhanded   c. farsighted   d. narrow-minded

38. **perpetuate** a family tradition
a. defend   b. observe   c. discontinue   d. question

39. **retrogress** in ability
a. fall behind   b. advance   c. fail   d. bask

40. the **placid** waters of the lake
a. peaceful   b. agitated   c. polluted   d. sparkling

41. made some very **trenchant** comments
a. revealing   b. strange   c. amusing   d. inane

42. **misconstrue** its meaning
a. question   b. understand   c. dislike   d. enjoy

43. **quell** an armed uprising
a. report   b. instigate   c. join   d. crush

44. a **voluminous** report
a. valuable   b. brief   c. learned   d. written

45. **disparaging** remarks
a. negative   b. unusual   c. tasteless   d. complimentary

46. since the plan appears to be **feasible**
a. uncomplicated   b. innocuous   c. unworkable   d. inexpensive

47. a truly **virulent** strain of the virus
a. unusual   b. mild   c. recent   d. deadly

48. a **suave** young man
a. clever   b. boorish   c. haughty   d. kindly

49. a **meticulous** worker
a. diligent   b. contented   c. retired   d. careless

50. with **negligible** results
a. substantial   b. curious   c. negative   d. unexpected

Definitions

Note carefully the spelling, pronunciation, and definition of each of the following words. Then write the word in the blank space in the illustrative phrase following.

1. **adulterate**
(ə 'dəl tə rāt)
(v.) to corrupt, make worse by the addition of something of lesser value
_____ the milk with water

2. **ambidextrous**
(am bi 'dek strəs)
(adj.) able to use both hands equally well; very skillful
marveled at his _____ ___ abilities

3. **augment**
(ôg 'ment)
(v.) to make larger, increase
got a job to _____ her income

4. **bereft**
(bi 'reft)
(part., adj.) deprived of; made unhappy through a loss
_____ of friends in his old age

5. **deploy**
(di 'ploi)
(v.) to position or arrange; to utilize
_____ troops for battle

6. **dour**
(daủr)
(adj.) stern, unyielding; gloomy, ill-humored
a _____ and sullen disposition

7. **fortitude**
('fôr ti tüd)
(n.) courage in facing difficulties
showed great _____ during the flood

8. **gape**
(gāp)
(v.) to stare with open mouth; to open the mouth wide; to open wide
_____ in wonder at the sight

9. **gibe**
(jīb)
(v.) to utter taunting words; (n.) an expression of scorn
_____ at him for his cowardice

10. **guise**
(gīz)
(n.) an external appearance, cover, mask
the _____ of a police officer

11. **insidious**
(in 'sid ē əs)
(adj.) designed or intended to deceive or entrap; sly, treacherous
an _____ scheme

12. **intimation**
(int ə 'mā shən)
(n.) a hint, indirect suggestion
gave no _____ of her financial difficulties

13. **opulent**
('äp yə lənt)
(adj.) wealthy, luxurious; ample
_____ living quarters in the palace

14. **pliable**
('plī ə bəl)
(adj.) easily bent, flexible; easily influenced
three spools of _____ copper wire

15. reiterate
(rē 'it ə rāt)

(*v.*) to say again, repeat

_____ a statement for emphasis

16. stolid
('stäl id)

(*adj.*) not easily moved, mentally or emotionally; dull, unresponsive

a _____ person who takes everything in stride

17. tentative
('ten tə tiv)

(*adj.*) experimental in nature; uncertain, hesitant

a _____ arrangement

18. unkempt
(ən 'kempt)

(*adj.*) not combed; untidy

seemed to take pride in being _____

19. verbatim
(vər 'bā təm)

(*adj., adv.*) word for word; exactly as written or spoken

repeat _____ to avoid any misunderstanding

20. warily
('wâr ə lē)

(*adv.*) cautiously, with great care

approach the mouth of the cave _____

Completing the Sentence

From the words for this unit, choose the one that best completes each of the following sentences. Write the word in the space provided.

1. At the risk of being boring, let me _____ my warning against careless driving.

2. In Shakespeare's famous tragedy *Othello*, Iago comes to Othello in the _____ of a friend but proves to be a deadly enemy.

3. Why would someone who is usually so neat and tidy appear in public in such a(n) _____ state?

4. America's earliest settlers faced the hardships of life on the frontier with _____ and faith.

5. Perhaps I would be bored with the _____ lifestyle of a millionaire, but I'm willing to try it.

6. Having learned to respect the power in his opponent's fists, the boxer circled _____ around the center of the ring.

7. The twigs that were to be woven into the basket were soaked in water to make them more _____.

8. How can you tell whether the chopped-meat patty you ate for lunch had been _____ with artificial coloring and other foreign substances?

12

9. We learned that beneath his _____ exterior there was a sensitive, highly subtle and perceptive mind.

10. The company commander called his troops together and asked for more volunteers to _____ the strength of the raiding party.

11. Since I need the speaker's exact words for my report, I have asked the stenographer to take down the speech _____.

12. His unchanging facial features and controlled voice as he received the news gave no _____ of his true feelings.

13. What a tragedy that in the twilight of her life the unfortunate woman should be _____ of all her loved ones!

14. Why should I be the object of all those _____ just because I'm wearing baby-blue Bermuda shorts on campus?

15. Many ballplayers can bat from either side of the plate, but they cannot throw well with each hand unless they are _____.

16. To this day, historians are still debating whether or not Aaron Burr was guilty of a(n) _____ plot to break up the United States.

17. Since his acceptance of the invitation was only _____, the hostess may be one man short at the dinner party.

18. The _____ expressions on the jurors' faces as they grimly filed back into the courtroom did not bode well for the defendant.

19. As the magician's beautiful blond assistant seemed to vanish into thin air, the entire audience _____ in amazement.

20. An experienced baseball manager _____ his outfielders according to the strengths or weaknesses of the opposing batters.

Synonyms   From the words for this unit, choose the one that is most nearly **the same** in meaning as each of the following groups of expressions. Write the word on the line given.

1. rich, lavish; plentiful, abundant _____

2. to ridicule, mock, deride, jeer _____

3. carefully, prudently, gingerly _____

4. to contaminate, pollute, sully _____

5. impassive, phlegmatic, unresponsive _____

6. a costume, semblance; a pretense _____

7. harsh, bleak, forbidding, saturnine _____

8. provisional, inconclusive _____

9. cunning, underhanded, perfidious _____

10. word for word, exact _____

11. sloppy, disheveled _____

12. resolve, steadfastness, mettle _____

13. supple, adaptable, resilient _____

14. a clue, indication, inkling _____

15. to arrange, station, organize _____

16. to gawk, ogle; to open wide _____

17. deprived; saddened by loss _____

18. equally skillful with both hands _____

19. to enlarge, supplement, amplify _____

20. to repeat, rehash _____

Antonyms *From the words for this unit, choose the one that is most nearly **opposite** in meaning to each of the following groups of expressions. Write the word on the line given.*

1. poverty-stricken, wretched, destitute _____

2. to decrease, diminish _____

3. cheery, inviting, genial _____

4. fearfulness, timidity, faintheartedness _____

5. rigid, inflexible, recalcitrant _____

6. definite, conclusive, confirmed _____

7. to purify, purge, expurgate _____

8. paraphrased _____

9. emotional, oversensitive; high-strung _____

10. frank, ingenuous, aboveboard _____

11. a compliment, praise _____

12. well-groomed, tidy, neat, natty _____

13. recklessly, heedlessly, incautiously _____

14. clumsy, all thumbs, maladroit _____

15. a direct or blunt communication _____

16. replete, well provided with _____

14

Choosing the Right Word   *Encircle the **boldface** word that more satisfactorily completes each of the following sentences.*

1. Recruits who complain of the cold should try to show a little more intestinal (**fortitude, intimation**) in facing the elements.

2. The young prince, who much preferred blue jeans, had to dress in the (**stolid, opulent**) robes designed for the coronation.

3. Though all hope of victory had faded, the remaining troops continued to resist the enemy with a (**bereft, dour**) tenacity.

4. The speaker (**deployed, adulterated**) all the facts and figures at her command to buttress her argument.

5. I soon found out that my supposed friend had taken it upon himself to repeat (**unkempt, verbatim**) every word I said about Frieda's party.

6. What a bore to hear the same silly advertising slogans (**gaped, reiterated**) endlessly on TV programs!

7. Do you believe that the curriculum will be (**stolid, adulterated**) if courses like driver education and consumer science are introduced?

8. The ticking grew louder as the bomb squad (**warily, pliably**) opened the package found on the grounds of the Governor's residence.

9. Let us not forget that the early fighters for women's rights were greeted with the (**gibes, guise**) of the unthinking mob.

10. What he calls his "(**insidious, pliable**) outlook on life" seems to me simply a lack of any firm moral standards.

11. A sort of heaviness in the air and an eerie silence were the first real (**reiterations, intimations**) of the approaching cyclone.

12. One of the chief reasons for his dateless weekends is undoubtedly his (**opulent, unkempt**) appearance.

13. There we were at the very edge of the cliff, with our front wheels about to plunge into a (**gaping, intimating**) ravine!

14. Do you expect me to listen to a lot of tired old ideas dressed up in the (**fortitude, guise**) of brilliant new insights?

15. In this scene of wild jubilation, my (**stolid, tentative**) roommate continued to eat his peanut butter sandwich as though nothing had happened.

16. Jane must have been (**bereft, disinclined**) of her senses when she bought that old car!

17. By studying the reactions of simpler life forms, researchers have greatly (**augmented, adulterated**) our knowledge of human behavior.

18. Because of my inexperience, I did not recognize at first his (**insidious, ambidextrous**) attempts to undermine our employer's confidence in me.

19. Have you heard the joke about the (**ambidextrous, opulent**) loafer who was equally adept at not working with either hand?

20. Because the situation is changing so rapidly, any plans we make to deal with the emergency can be no more than (**verbatim, tentative**).

Definitions

Note carefully the spelling, pronunciation, and definition of each of the following words. Then write the word in the blank space in the illustrative phrase following.

1. adroit
(ə 'droit)

(*adj.*) skillful, expert in the use of the hands or mind

_____ at twirling a rope

2. amicable
('am ə kə bəl)

(*adj.*) peaceable, friendly

an _____ settlement of the dispute

3. averse
(ə 'vərs)

(*adj.*) having a deep-seated distaste; opposed, unwilling

_____ to strenuous exercise

4. belligerent
(bə 'lij ə rənt)

(*adj.*) given to fighting, warlike; (*n.*) one at war, one engaged in war

a _____ answer

5. benevolent
(bə 'nev ə lənt)

(*adj.*) kindly, charitable

a _____ feeling toward all their neighbors

6. cursory
('kər sə rē)

(*adj.*) hasty, not thorough

a _____ glance at the document

7. duplicity
(dü 'plis ə tē)

(*n.*) treachery, deceitfulness

fired the employees suspected of _____

8. extol
(ek 'stōl)

(*v.*) to praise extravagantly

_____ her heroic deeds

9. feasible
('fē zə bəl)

(*adj.*) possible, able to be done

develop a _____ plan of action

10. grimace
('grim əs)

(*n.*) a wry face, facial distortion; (*v.*) to make a wry face

a _____ of pain

11. holocaust
('häl ə kôst)

(*n.*) a large-scale destruction, especially by fire; a vast slaughter

a victim of the Chicago _____

12. impervious
(im 'pər vē əs)

(*adj.*) not affected or hurt by; admitting of no passage or entrance

a plastic cover _____ to moisture

13. impetus
('im pə təs)

(*n.*) a moving force, impulse, stimulus

gave a new _____ to the drive

14. jeopardy
('jep ər dē)

(*n.*) danger

mistakes that put the entire operation in serious

_____

15. meticulous
(mə 'tik yə ləs)

(*adj.*) extremely careful; particular about details

a _____ housekeeper

16. nostalgia
(nä 'stal jə)

(*n.*) a longing for something past; homesickness

a vague feeling of _____

17. quintessence
(kwin 'tes əns)

(*n.*) the purest essence or form of something; the most typical example

a deed hailed as the _____ of valor

18. retrogress
(re trə 'gres)

(*v.*) to move backward; to return to an earlier condition

has _____ into barbarism

19. scrutinize
('skrüt ə nīz)

(*v.*) to examine closely

_____ the documents

20. tepid
('tep id)

(*adj.*) lukewarm; unenthusiastic, marked by an absence of interest

a cup of _____ tea

Completing the Sentence

From the words for this unit, choose the one that best completes each of the following sentences. Write the word in the space provided.

1. As the old soldier watched the parade pass by, he was suddenly filled with _____ for the youthful years he had spent in the Army.

2. An expert from the museum _____ the painting, looking for telltale signs that would prove it to be genuine or expose it as a forgery.

3. My teacher counseled me to keep up my studies, or my performance in class might once again _____ into mediocrity.

4. Only when we learned that the embezzler had tried to cast suspicion on his innocent partner did we realize the extent of his _____.

5. The physical education instructor _____ the virtues of regular exercise.

6. If you are _____ to hard study and intensive reading, how do you expect to get through law school?

7. King Arthur's Knights of the Round Table were the _____ of chivalry.

8. We must not forget the millions of people who were ruthlessly slaughtered by the Nazis in the _____ of the 1940s.

9. Miss De Carlo's records—neat, accurate, and complete in every respect— show that she is a most _____ worker.

10. For centuries, Switzerland has avoided becoming a(n) _____ in the wars that have scarred the rest of Europe.

11. Looking forward to a hot bath, I was disappointed at the feeble stream of _____ water that flowed into the tub.

12. Percy shows no particular talent as a worker, but I must admit that he is exceptionally _____ at finding excuses for not doing his job.

13. My teammates agreed that a triple reverse looked mighty impressive on the chalkboard but doubted that the play would prove _____ on the football field.

14. If, as you claim, you really like raw oysters, why do you make such an eloquent _____ every time you swallow one?

15. When I realized how bad the brakes of the old car were, I feared that our lives were in _____ .

16. No one doubts the _____ intentions of the program for community improvement, but it was ruined by mismanagement.

17. When I heard Rose speaking French so fluently, my determination to master that language received a fresh _____ .

18. Regarding native Americans as "bloodthirsty savages," Europeans were rarely able to maintain _____ relations with them.

19. A(n) _____ examination of my luggage was enough to show me that someone had been tampering with it.

20. What good is a plastic raincoat that is _____ to water if it also prevents any body heat from escaping?

Synonyms *From the words for this unit, choose the one that is most nearly **the same** in meaning as each of the following groups of expressions. Write the word on the line given.*

1. quick, superficial, perfunctory _____

2. careful, fastidious, painstaking, fussy _____

3. risk, hazard, peril _____

4. workable, practicable, viable _____

5. to revert; to degenerate, decline _____

6. fraud, double-dealing, chicanery _____

7. a conflagration; devastation; annihilation _____

8. a longing for things past; homesickness _____

9. impenetrable; resistant, proof against _____

10. an impulse, incentive, stimulus, spur _____

11. disinclined, opposed, loath _____

12. congenial, neighborly, cordial _____

13. a pained expression, facial contortion _____

14. lukewarm; insipid; halfhearted, wishy-washy _____

15. the purest essence; a paragon, exemplar _____

16. kindly, benign, well-meaning _____

17. to inspect, examine, pore over _____

18. clever, deft, dexterous, slick _____

19. to glorify, applaud, acclaim, hail _____

20. aggressive, combative, pugnacious _____

Antonyms From the words for this unit, choose the one that is most nearly **opposite** in meaning to each of the following groups of expressions. Write the word on the line given.

1. to criticize, belittle, disparage _____

2. safety, security _____

3. unworkable, impractical _____

4. thorough, painstaking, careful _____

5. a curb, hindrance, impediment, constraint _____

6. favorably disposed, eager, keen _____

7. heated, excited, enthusiastic _____

8. hostile, antagonistic _____

9. to skim, scan, glance at _____

10. clumsy, inept, all thumbs _____

11. malicious, spiteful, malevolent _____

12. to advance, evolve, progress _____

13. peaceful, conciliatory, placid _____

14. porous, permeable, vulnerable _____

15. careless, negligent, sloppy _____

16. a deluge, inundation _____

17. to smile, beam, grin _____

Choosing the Right Word

*Encircle the **boldface** word that more satisfactorily completes each of the following sentences*

1. Because I was not even born when the Beatles were at the height of their popularity, their albums do not fill me with (**duplicity, nostalgia**).

2. Though it may appear rather ordinary to the casual observer, Lincoln's Gettysburg Address is to me the (**impetus, quintessence**) of eloquence.

3. Some civil engineers believe that within a generation it will be (**feasible, benevolent**) to derive a large part of our energy directly from the sun.

4. The nightmare that continues to haunt all thoughtful people is a nuclear (**holocaust, jeopardy**) in which our civilization might be destroyed.

5. It made me very uncomfortable to see with what suspicion the wary customs officer (**scrutinized, extolled**) my passport.

6. In the Sherlock Holmes stories, we read of the evil Professor Moriarty, whose (**duplicity, impetus**) was almost a match for Holmes' genius.

7. Though peace talks began with an exchange of lofty sentiments, they soon (**retrogressed, scrutinized**) into petty squabbling and backbiting.

8. I knew she would be (**impervious, meticulous**) in caring for my plants, but I didn't expect her to water them with a medicine dropper!

9. Anyone who is (**averse, cursory**) to having a girls' basketball team in our school doesn't know what's been happening in recent years.

10. (**Extolling, Scrutinizing**) other people's achievements is fine, but it is no substitute for doing something remarkable of your own.

11. Providing a powerful defense force for our nation does not mean that we are taking a (**belligerent, meticulous**) attitude toward any other nation.

12. When I saw my sister land in a tree on her first parachute jump, my interest in learning to skydive became decidedly (**tepid, adroit**).

13. After shouting at each other rather angrily, the participants in the round-table discussion calmed down and parted (**feasibly, amicably**).

14. It was rude of you to (**retrogress, grimace**) so obviously when the speaker mispronounced words and made grammatical errors.

15. The lawyer's (**adroit, cursory**) questioning slowly but surely revealed the weaknesses in his opponent's case.

16. Carelessness in even minor details may (**averse, jeopardize**) the success of a major theatrical production.

17. News of famine in various parts of the world has given added (**nostalgia, impetus**) to the drive to increase food production.

18. His parents tried to encourage an interest in literature, music, and art, but he seemed (**amicable, impervious**) to such influences.

19. Do you think you are being fair in passing judgment on Fran's poem after such a (**cursory, benevolent**) reading?

20. On the morning of the picnic, the sky was gray and overcast, but suddenly the sun came out and smiled on us (**benevolently, adroitly**).

Definitions

Note carefully the spelling, pronunciation, and definition of each of the following words. Then write the word in the blank space in the illustrative phrase following.

1. **adversary**
   ('ad vər ser ē)

   (*n.*) an enemy, opponent

   a worthy _____ on the handball court

2. **alienate**
   ('ā lē ə nāt)

   (*v.*) to turn away; to make indifferent or hostile

   bad habits that _____ friends

3. **artifice**
   ('är tə fis)

   (*n.*) a skillful or ingenious device; a clever trick; clever skill; trickery

   deceived by his _____

4. **coerce**
   (kō 'ərs)

   (*v.*) to compel, force

   _____ into obedience by a threat of punishment

5. **craven**
   ('krā vən)

   (*adj.*) cowardly; (*n.*) a coward

   criticized by his opponent for his _____ policies

6. **culinary**
   ('kyü lə ner ē)

   (*adj.*) of or related to cooking or to the kitchen

   a fine example of French _____ art

7. **delete**
   (di 'lēt)

   (*v.*) to erase, wipe out, cut out

   shortened the report by _____ two paragraphs

8. **demise**
   (di 'mīz)

   (*n.*) a death, especially of a person in a lofty position

   tolling bells that indicated the _____ of the king

9. **exhilarate**
   (eg 'zil ə rāt)

   (*v.*) to enliven, cheer, give spirit or liveliness to

   _____ by the good news

10. **fallow**
    ('fal ō)

    (*adj.*) unseeded or untilled; inactive

    garden plots intentionally left _____ for a year

11. **harass**
    ('har əs)

    (*v.*) to disturb, worry; to trouble by repeated attacks

    _____ the witness with difficult questions

12. **inclement**
    (in 'klem ənt)

    (*adj.*) stormy, harsh; severe in attitude or action

    unaccustomed to the _____ New England winter

13. **muse**
    (myüz)

    (*v.*) to think about in a dreamy way, ponder

    _____ on the meaning of life

4. negligible
('neg lə jə bəl)

(*adj.*) so unimportant that it can be disregarded

a _____ loss that we need not worry about

5. perpetuate
(pər 'pech ü āt)

(*v.*) to make permanent or long lasting

_____ the customs of our ancestors

6. precedent
('pres ə dənt)

(*n.*) an example that may serve as a basis for imitation or later action

set a _____ for others to follow

7. punitive
('pyü nə tiv)

(*adj.*) inflicting or aiming at punishment

led a _____ expedition against the rebels

8. redress
(rē 'dres)

(*v.*) to set right, remedy; (*n.*) relief from wrong or injury

seek _____ through the courts

9. sojourn
('sō jərn)

(*n.*) a temporary stay; (*v.*) to stay for a time

a week's _____ in Paris

20. urbane
(ər 'bān)

(*adj.*) refined in manner or style, suave

an _____ host

Completing the Sentence

From the words for this unit, choose the one that best completes each of the following sentences. Write the word in the space provided.

1. Coach Groh took me off the starting team as a(n) _____ measure for missing two days of practice.

2. The deserted buildings and the fields lying _____ hinted at the troubles the farmers in the area were undergoing.

3. When the snowstorm lasted into a second day, we listened attentively to the radio to find out if our school was among those closed because of the

_____ weather.

4. David's charmingly _____ manner and keen wit made him a much sought-after guest at social gatherings.

5. The _____ of an administration in the United States is never a crisis because a newly elected administration is waiting to take over.

6. The full extent of my _____ skill is preparing scrambled eggs on toast.

7. When planning our trip to the Southwest, we made sure to set aside two

days for a(n) _____ at the Grand Canyon.

8. Since both cars had virtually come to a halt by the time their bumpers met,

the damage was _____ .

9. Their _____ behavior at the first sign of danger was a disgrace to the uniform they wore.

10. When citizens feel that something is wrong, they have a right under the First Amendment to ask their government for a(n) _____ of grievances.

11. I advise you to _____ from your statement all the words th[ ] people are likely to find personally offensive.

12. In 1858, Abraham Lincoln held a series of debates with Stephen Dougla[s] his _____ in the contest for U.S. Senator from Illinois.

13. The coach emphasized that the way to stop our opponent's passing gam[ ] was to _____ their receivers and "blitz" their quarterback.

14. When Grandfather stubbornly refused to eat his vegetables, he set a(n) _____ that was immediately followed by the children.

15. His bad manners and insufferable conceit _____ even tho[ ] who were most inclined to judge him favorably.

16. If we continue to elect unworthy people to public office, we will simply _____ the evils that we have tried so hard to correct.

17. Magicians rely on sleight of hand and other forms of _____ to deceive their unsuspecting audiences.

18. There are far more subtle ways of _____ a person into doing what you want than twisting his or her arm.

19. As he lay under the old apple tree, he began to _____ on the strange twists of fate that had led to the present situation.

20. At first we watched the game with relatively little emotion, but we becam[e] so _____ by our team's strong comeback that we began [ ] cheer loudly.

Synonyms   From the words for this unit, choose the one that is m[o] nearly **the same** in meaning as each of the following groups of expressions. Write the word on the line provided at the right.

1. to stimulate, excite, gladden _____

2. blustery, tempestuous, implacable _____

3. fearful, fainthearted, pusillanimous _____

4. suave, elegant _____

5. an antagonist, rival, foe _____

6. to annoy, pester, bedevil, beleaguer, worry _____

7. to rectify, correct, mitigate _____

8. trivial, inconsequential, insignificant _____

9. to remove, cancel, expunge _____

10. penalizing, retaliatory _____

11. to meditate, contemplate, daydream _____

12. to separate, drive apart, estrange _____

13. a visit, stopover, brief stay _____

14. unproductive, inert, dormant _____

15. to continue, preserve, prolong indefinitely _____

16. a death, decease, passing away _____

17. to pressure, bully, intimidate, constrain _____

18. a guide, tradition, model _____

19. a ruse, stratagem, contrivance _____

20. related to cooking _____

Antonyms   *From the words for this unit, choose the one that is most nearly* **opposite** *in meaning to each of the following groups of expressions. Write the word on the line provided at the right.*

1. crude, uncouth, boorish _____

2. brave, courageous, valiant _____

3. significant, crucial, momentous _____

4. discourage, dispirit, dishearten, inhibit _____

5. mild, gentle, balmy, tranquil _____

6. a friend, ally, supporter, confederate _____

7. to discontinue, abolish, abandon _____

8. to befriend, attract, captivate; to reconcile _____

9. productive, fertile, prolific _____

0. to insert, add, retain, include _____

1. a birth, beginning, commencement _____

2. that which follows or comes afterward _____

3. to persuade, cajole _____

Choosing the Right Word   *Encircle the **boldface** word that more satisfactorily completes each of the following sentences.*

1. After a long (**urbane, fallow**) period during which she scarcely touched her brushes, the painter suddenly produced a series of major canvases.

2. May I remind you that the (**punitive, amicable**) action we are authorized to take does not include physical force of any kind.

3. We must reject the (**craven, fallow**) advice of those who feel we can solve social problems by abandoning our democratic freedoms.

4. It is all very well to (**muse, perpetuate**) on what might have happened, but far better to take action to make good things happen.

5. The critics unanimously praised the actor for the (**urbane, negligible**) charm with which he played the well-bred English gentleman.

6. When Washington refused to serve a third term as President, he set a(n) (**precedent, artifice**) that was to last for 150 years.

7. We need a foreman who can maintain good discipline in the shop without (**harassing, exhilarating**) the workers.

8. Because of the severe sentences he often handed down, he gained the reputation of being an extremely (**inclement, negligible**) judge.

9. I want to know by whose authority my name was (**deleted, coerced**) from the list of students eligible to take the scholarship examinations.

10. When he blocked my jump shot, took the rebound, drove down the court, and scored, I realized that I was facing a worthy (**artifice, adversary**).

11. If we do not take steps now to clear his name, we will be (**perpetuating, redressing**) an injustice that has already lasted far too long.

12. Our city government needs basic reforms; clever little (**precedents, artifices**) will not solve our problems.

13. I admit that we did some foolish things after the game, but you must remember how (**mused, exhilarated**) we were by the victory.

14. Do you really expect me to believe that your friends (**coerced, alienated**) you into cutting class to go to the movies?

15. Only when the attempt to get the British government to (**redress, harass**) injustices proved unsuccessful did the American colonists resort to arms.

16. Our history shows how the (**demise, artifice**) of one political party provided an opportunity for the formation of a new one.

17. The highlight of my trip to Europe came when I (**sojourned, redressed**) in the birthplace of my ancestors.

18. And now I want you all to try my (**inclement, culinary**) masterpiece—a salami souffle, garnished with sour cream.

19. Since we are making (**negligible, craven**) progress in our fight against pollution, the time has come for us to adopt completely new methods.

Coach Gates ran the risk of (**exhilarating, alienating**) influential graduates of the school when he suspended a star player who had broken training.

Analogies   *In each of the following, encircle the item that best completes the comparison.*

1. dour is to **cheery** as
a. stolid is to impervious
b. amicable is to pliable
c. fallow is to productive
d. inclement is to belligerent

2. averse is to **reluctant** as
a. adroit is to dexterous
b. insidious is to benevolent
c. verbatim is to oral
d. culinary is to tepid

3. delete is to **insert** as
a. muse is to ponder
b. decrease is to augment
c. harass is to frighten
d. coerce is to compel

4. duplicity is to **unfavorable** as
a. fortitude is to favorable
b. intimation is to unfavorable
c. demise is to favorable
d. precedent is to unfavorable

5. adversary is to **friendly** as
a. peacemaker is to belligerent
b. juggler is to ambidextrous
c. orphan is to bereft
d. coward is to craven

6. meticulous is to **cursory** as
a. adulterated is to unkempt
b. warily is to cautiously
c. appreciable is to negligible
d. tentative is to feasible

7. unkempt is to **appearance** as
a. tepid is to height
b. urbane is to manner
c. impervious is to complexion
d. stolid is to weight

8. virtue is to **extol** as
a. accomplishment is to gibe
b. duplicity is to honor
c. right is to redress
d. vice is to deplore

9. lawyer is to **legal** as
a. sculptor is to naval
b. politician is to punitive
c. athlete is to intellectual
d. chef is to culinary

10. gape is to **wide** as
a. yawn is to narrow
b. frown is to wide
c. squint is to narrow
d. blink is to wide

11. exhilarate is to **uplift** as
a. scrutinize is to expand
b. alienate is to befriend
c. sojourn is to restrain
d. adulterate is to debase

12. insidious is to **unfavorable** as
a. benevolent is to favorable
b. meticulous is to unfavorable
c. craven is to favorable
d. ambidextrous is to unfavorable

13. hovel is to **poverty** as
a. apartment is to artifice
b. palace is to opulence
c. fort is to jeopardy
d. cave is to quintessence

14. flood is to **water** as
a. avalanche is to wind
b. holocaust is to fire
c. hurricane is to ice
d. tornado is to snow

15. precedent is to **before** as
a. intimation is to after
b. redress is to before
c. consequence is to after
d. retrogression is to before

16. smile is to **grimace** as
a. laugh is to cry
b. sneeze is to yawn
c. weep is to bewail
d. wink is to blink

17. reiterate is to **repeat** as
a. extol is to criticize
b. perpetuate is to commit
c. scrutinize is to muse
d. deploy is to arrange

18. sponge is to **impervious** as
a. glass is to brittle
b. wall is to rigid
c. umbrella is to porous
d. belt is to pliable

26

19. nostalgia is to **sad** as
a. adversity is to joyful
b. impetus is to sad
c. exhilaration is to joyful
d. guise is to sad

20. wary is to **caution** as
a. stolid is to insight
b. meticulous is to care
c. cursory is to diligence
d. tentative is to firmness

Spelling All of the following words, correctly spelled, were introduced in Units 1–3. Underline the word that is **incorrectly** spelled in each of the following groups. Then supply the correct spelling in the space provided.

1. artifice	pliable	advesary	___
2. exhilirate	craven	amicable	___
3. tentitive	impetus	redress	___
4. harrass	duplicity	adroit	___
5. jeapordy	nostalgia	feasible	___
6. fortitude	unkemt	sojourn	___
7. grimace	opulent	ambidexterous	___
8. holocost	perpetuate	bereft	___
9. extoll	averse	punitive	___
10. gape	verbatim	insideous	___
11. intimation	muse	benevalent	___
12. adulterate	cursery	precedent	___
13. stolid	quintescence	alienate	___
14. neglegible	deploy	urbane	___
15. inclement	delete	coerse	___

Identification In each of the following groups, encircle the word that is best defined or suggested by the introductory phrase.

1. stare at in amazement
a. gape   b. grimace   c. redress   d. harass

2. emphasize by repetition
a. scrutinize   b. reiterate   c. gibe   d. tepid

3. not easily moved to emotion
a. meticulous   b. stolid   c. impervious   d. feasible

4. a deceptive appearance
a. nostalgia   b. redress   c. craven   d. guise

5. showing extreme attention to details
a. meticulous   b. adroit   c. punitive   d. negligible

6. one step forward, two steps back
a. reiterate   b. ambidextrous   c. retrogress   d. delete

7. "The King is dead. Long live the King!"
a. jeopardy   b. demise   c. duplicity   d. adversary

8. a facial expression that shows a negative reaction
a. redress   b. grimace   c. artifice   d. intimation

9. "That guy is chicken-hearted."
a. fortitude   b. adversary   c. verbatim   d. craven

10. widespread destruction
a. muse   b. grimace   c. duplicity   d. holocaust

11. harmful, but in a rather attractive way
a. insidious   b. cursory   c. heedless   d. dour

12. the purest of the pure
a. nostalgia   b. artifice   c. intimation   d. quintessence

13. said of a "double-dealer"
a. intimation   b. duplicity   c. precedent   d. adversary

14. look over carefully and critically
a. perpetuate   b. scrutinize   c. alienate   d. reiterate

15. payment for a scratched fender from the person responsible
a. redress   b. fortitude   c. holocaust   d. grimace

16. tease with mocking words
a. muse   b. delete   c. coerce   d. gibe

17. neither hot nor cold
a. craven   b. averse   c. tepid   d. ambidextrous

18. a one-week stay in Athens
a. sojourn   b. precedent   c. reiteration   d. jeopardy

19. cause to last indefinitely
a. provoke   b. harass   c. coerce   d. perpetuate

20. driving force
a. jeopardy   b. nostalgia   c. grimace   d. impetus

Antonyms   In each of the following groups, encircle the word or expression that is most nearly the **opposite** of the first word in **boldface type**.

1. adulterate
a. lose
b. harass
c. purify
d. cheat

2. extol
a. improve
b. criticize
c. charge
d. analyze

3. cursory
a. blasphemous
b. brave
c. speedy
d. thorough

4. craven
a. stuffed
b. yielding
c. brave
d. tidy

5. adroit
a. friendly
b. bereft
c. smooth
d. clumsy

6. feasible
a. cheap
b. glum
c. impractical
d. delicious

7. inclement
a. pleasant
b. strange
c. boring
d. tasty

8. warily
a. rashly
b. softly
c. quietly
d. angrily

9. amicable
a. quarrelsome
b. friendly
c. easy
d. intellectual

10. adversary
a. accuser
b. enemy
c. relative
d. ally

11. perpetuate
a. soothe
b. discontinue
c. anger
d. commit

12. verbatim
a. nominal
b. pleasing
c. adapted
d. delayed

13. urbane
a. crude
b. rural
c. weak
d. irrelevant

14. opulent
a. unkind
b. wretched
c. rich
d. small

15. augment
a. insult
b. reduce
c. predict
d. annoy

16. unkempt
a. bound
b. punctual
c. neat
d. shiny

17. exhilarate
a. accuse
b. depress
c. excite
d. worsen

18. pliable
a. consumable
b. straight
c. demanding
d. rigid

19. retrogress
a. agree
b. advance
c. eject
d. permit

20. averse
a. favorable
b. safe
c. unwilling
d. joyous

Completing the Sentence

From the following list of words choose the one that best completes each of the sentences below. Write the word in the appropriate space.

Group A

bereft	impetus	precedent	inclement
guise	jeopardy	holocaust	ambidextrous
stolid	intimation	grimace	averse

1. There is no historical _____ for the new policy she proposes to introduce.

2. When I saw the quarterback throw passes with his left hand as well as his right, I realized that he was _____ .

3. The only way I can explain his senseless conduct is that grief left him _____ of his usual good judgment.

4. The speaker warned that unless we can find adequate and dependable sources of energy, the very existence of our society may be placed in _____ .

5. When he told me of his recent conversation with Yvonne, I had my first _____ of why I had not been invited to the party.

Group B

impervious	belligerent	artifice	extol
scrutinize	alienated	insidious	tepid
duplicity	nostalgia	gape	gibes

1. After finishing the last problem, I carefully _____ the entire exam for any errors I might have overlooked.

2. His tasteless flattery _____ the very people he was trying so hard to impress favorably.

3. After trying unsuccessfully to explain to him why his driving habits are bad, I have decided that he is _____ to criticism and instruction.

4. She bore their _____ with such good nature and patience that they soon gave up and looked for someone else to make fun of.

5. We must be prepared to resist the _____ influence of his disguised racial prejudice.

Word Families

A. *On the line provided write a **noun form** of each of the following words.*

EXAMPLE: insidious—**insidiousness**

1. retrogress _____
2. feasible _____
3. perpetuate _____
4. adroit _____
5. tentative _____
6. warily _____
7. opulent _____
8. harass _____
9. benevolent _____
10. adulterate _____
11. urbane _____
12. scrutinize _____
13. alienate _____
14. coerce _____
15. delete _____
16. exhilarate _____

B. *On the line provided, write a **verb** related to each of the following words.*

EXAMPLE: precedent—**precede**

1. intimation _____
2. negligible _____
3. bereft _____
4. jeopardy _____
5. punitive _____

**Filling
the Blanks**

*Encircle the pair of words that best complete the
meaning of each of the following passages.*

1. "I haven't yet had the time to give your latest sales report more than a
_____ glance," my boss told me. "However, I plan to
_____ it carefully before we sit down to discuss it in detail."

   a. verbatim . . . reiterate
   b. cursory . . . scrutinize
   c. meticulous . . . augment
   d. tentative . . . redress

2. Tony's general attitude toward people is so _____ that he
has _____ absolutely everybody who knows him. If he didn't
walk around with such a huge chip on his shoulder, he would have a few
friends.

   a. benevolent . . . deployed
   b. adversary . . . exhilarated
   c. belligerent . . . alienated
   d. amicable . . . redressed

3. Some people always stick up their noses at food they're not accustomed
to, but I'm not at all _____ to trying something new. Still,
experience has taught me to be _____ of such dubious
delicacies as chocolate-covered ants, and I usually "look before I leap,"
so to speak.

   a. amicable . . . bereft
   b. tepid . . . negligible
   c. averse . . . wary
   d. impervious . . . craven

4. I want to use an excerpt from the President's inaugural address in my
report. Unfortunately, the passage I want is far too long to reproduce
_____ . To get it down to the size I need, I'll have to
_____ part of it.

   a. tentatively . . . augment
   b. stolidly . . . coerce
   c. meticulously . . . reiterate
   d. verbatim . . . delete

5. My first _____ of Nelson's double-dealing came when I
discovered him whispering with my opponent. Prior to that, I had no inkling
of my so-called friend's _____ .

   a. intimation . . . duplicity
   b. scrutiny . . . fortitude
   c. precedent . . . artifice
   d. redress . . . coercion

6. Because the course of the disease was so _____ , we
didn't notice at first that the patient's condition was no longer improving
but in fact had begun to _____ .

   a. tentative . . . adulterate
   b. adroit . . . redress
   c. averse . . . perpetuate
   d. insidious . . . retrogress

Definitions	Note carefully the spelling, pronunciation, and definition of each of the following words. Then write the word in the blank space in the illustrative phrase following.

1. affiliated
(ə 'fil ē āt əd)

(*adj., part.*) associated, connected

_____ with a well-known law firm

2. ascertain
(as ər 'tān)

(*v.*) to find out

_____ what the cost will be

3. attainment
(ə 'tān mənt)

(*n.*) an accomplishment; the act of achieving

a man of high literary _____

4. bequeath
(bi 'kwēth)

(*v.*) to give or pass on as an inheritance

has _____ a fortune to his widow

5. cogent
('kō jint)

(*adj.*) forceful, convincing

a _____ plea for prison reform

6. converge
(kən 'verj)

(*v.*) to move toward one point, approach nearer together

as the delegates _____ on the hall

7. disperse
(di 'spərs)

(*v.*) to scatter, spread far and wide

order the police to _____ the crowd

8. esteem
(es 'tēm)

(*v.*) to regard highly; (*n.*) a highly favorable opinion or judgment

someone we all hold in high _____

9. expunge
(ik 'spənj)

(*v.*) to erase, obliterate, destroy

ordered the offending remarks _____ from the court record

10. finite
('fī nīt)

(*adj.*) having limits; lasting for a limited time

a _____ number of possibilities

11. invulnerable
(in 'vəl nər ə bəl)

(*adj.*) not able to be wounded or hurt; shielded against attack

an _____ fortress

12. malevolent
(mə 'lev ə lənt)

(*adj.*) spiteful, showing ill will

told a _____ lie

13. nonchalant
(nän shə 'länt)

(*adj.*) cool and confident, unconcerned

walked down the street with a _____ air

14. omniscient
(äm 'nish ənt)

(*adj.*) knowing everything; having unlimited awareness or understanding

a professor who seemed to be _____

32

15. panacea
(pan ə 'sē ə)

(*n.*) a remedy for all ills, cure-all; an answer to all problems

a _____ for all our problems

16. scrupulous
('skrü pyə ləs)

(*adj.*) exact, careful, attending thoroughly to details; having high moral standards

describe with _____ accuracy

17. skulk
(skəlk)

(*v.*) to move about stealthily; to lie in hiding

a burglar _____ in an alley

18. supercilious
(sü pər 'sil ē əs)

(*adj.*) proud and contemptuous; showing scorn because of a feeling of superiority

took a _____ attitude toward the servants

19. uncanny
(ən 'kan ē)

(*adj.*) strange, mysterious, weird, beyond explanation

an _____ skill at playing bridge

20. venial
('vē nē əl)

(*adj.*) easily excused; pardonable

a _____ offense

Completing the Sentence

From the words for this unit, choose the one that best completes each of the following sentences. Write the word in the space provided.

1. Her ability to guess what I am thinking about at any given time is nothing short of _____ .

2. So long as we remained indoors, we were _____ to the Arctic blasts that swept down on our snowbound cabin.

3. The more knowledge and wisdom people acquire, the more keenly they become aware that no one is _____ .

4. Because our natural resources are _____ and by no means inexhaustible, we must learn to conserve them.

5. We refer to antibiotics as "wonder drugs," but we must realize that they are not _____ for all the physical ailments of mankind.

6. Our representative offered one simple but _____ argument against the proposal—it would raise the cost of living.

7. Isn't it remarkable how quickly a throng of sunbathers will pick up their belongings and _____ when a few drops of rain fall?

8. Is there anyone in the world as _____ as a senior who attends a mere sophomore class dance?

9. Her election to Congress was the _____ of a lifelong ambition.

10. As we stood on the railway tracks looking off into the distance, the rails seemed to _____ and meet at some far-off point.

11. Only by paying _____ attention to innumerable details were we able to piece together the cause of the accident.

12. The screening committee investigated not only the candidate himself but also the organizations with which he was _____ .

13. Before making our final plans, we should _____ exactly how much money we will have for expenses.

14. Though I wanted to "let bygones be bygones," I found that I could not wholly _____ the bitter memory of their behavior from my mind.

15. When I saw the pain he caused others and the pleasure he took in doing so, I realized he was a truly _____ person.

16. If only parents could _____ their hard-won practical wisdom and experience to their children!

17. In a situation that would have left me all but helpless with embarrassment, he remained cool and _____ .

18. I knew the dean would accept my apology when she characterized my behavior as thoughtless but _____ .

19. When the candidate admitted openly that he had been mistaken in some of his earlier policies, we _____ him more highly than ever.

20. In the opening scene of the horror film a shadowy figure dressed in black _____ through the graveyard in the moonlight.

Synonyms   *From the words for this unit, choose the one that is most nearly **the same** in meaning as each of the following groups of expressions. Write the word on the line provided at the right.*

1. snobbish, patronizing, overbearing   _____

2. painstaking, meticulous, conscientious   _____

3. composed, unruffled, indifferent, blasé   _____

4. to lurk, slink, prowl   _____

5. to hand down, transmit, bestow   _____

6. to respect, admire, honor, revere   _____

7. malicious, wicked, sinister, malignant   _____

8. impregnable, impervious, immune   _____

9. eerie, inexplicable, spooky   _____

10. attached, related, joined to   _____

11. to meet, unite, intersect, merge   _____

12. a universal cure; an easy solution   _____

13. to delete, efface, annihilate   _____

14. persuasive, compelling   _____

15. wise, all-knowing   _____

16. excusable, forgivable   _____

17. to discover, determine, establish, find out   _____

18. limited, bounded, measurable   _____

19. an achievement, fulfillment   _____

20. to break up, scatter, dispel   _____

Antonyms   *From the words for this unit, choose the one that is most nearly* **opposite** *in meaning to each of the following groups of expressions. Write the word on the line provided at the right.*

1. ignorant, unknowing   _____

2. careless, negligent, remiss; dishonest   _____

3. disdain, scorn, contempt   _____

4. kind, benevolent, compassionate   _____

5. a failure, defeat; frustration   _____

6. to collect, congregate, assemble, muster   _____

7. exposed, unprotected, defenseless   _____

8. unlimited, immeasurable; everlasting, eternal   _____

9. humble, meek, deferential, servile   _____

10. perturbed, agitated, disconcerted, abashed   _____

11. unconvincing, weak, ineffective; irrelevant   _____

12. unpardonable, unforgivable, inexcusable   _____

13. unconnected, dissociated   _____

14. to diverge, separate, go separate ways   _____

15. to insert; to mark, imprint, impress   _____

Choosing the Right Word

*Encircle the **boldface** word that more satisfactorily completes each of the following sentences.*

1. At first, the two candidates were in disagreement on every issue, but as the campaign went on, their opinions seemed to (**disperse, converge**).

2. Is it true that some dogs have a(n) (**uncanny, malevolent**) sense of the approach of death?

3. When I found myself flushed with anger, I realized that I was not so (**scrupulous, invulnerable**) to his bitter sarcasm as I had thought I was!

4. Though Mr. Darden has spend years studying African history, he does not claim to be (**omniscient, cogent**) in that field.

5. The critic recognized the book's faults but dismissed them as (**venial, uncanny**) in view of the author's overall achievement.

6. As a member of the grand jury, it is your duty to be (**supercilious, scrupulous**) in weighing every detail of evidence.

7. The reform candidate vowed to root out the corruption that (**bequeathed, skulked**) through the corridors of City Hall.

8. The newspaper revealed that the city's chief building inspector was (**converged, affiliated**) with a large construction company.

9. Her elegant clothes and (**finite, supercilious**) manner did not conceal the fact that she was our old friend, Beulah Blitz, a former waitress.

10. Instead of making an "informed guess," why not (**ascertain, esteem**) exactly how many students are going on the trip to Washington?

11. Lincoln said, "If you once forfeit the confidence of your fellow citizens, you can never regain their respect and (**esteem, attainment**)."

12. We found her criticism of our conduct unpleasant, but we had to admit that her remarks were (**venial, cogent**) and to the point.

13. Instead of blaming a (**malevolent, invulnerable**) fate for your failures, why not look for the causes within yourself?

14. There are so many different factors involved in an energy crisis that no single measure can be expected to serve as a(n) (**panacea, attainment**).

15. He is the kind of person who has many (**convergences, attainments**) but seems unable to put them to any practical use.

16. Nothing he may (**disperse, bequeath**) to the next generation can be more precious than the memory of his long life of honorable public service.

17. Though the journey seemed interminable, I knew that it was (**cogent, finite**) and that I would soon be home.

18. Her bright, optimistic manner did much to (**converge, disperse**) the atmosphere of gloom that had settled over the meeting.

19. When I splattered paint on my art teacher, I tried to appear (**nonchalant, malevolent**) but succeeded only in looking horrified.

20. Scientists still debate whether it was a sudden catastrophe or a natural process that (**expunged, converged**) dinosaurs from the face of the earth.

Definitions

Note carefully the spelling, pronunciation, and definition of each of the following words. Then write the word in the blank space in the illustrative phrase following.

1. altruistic
(al trü ′is tik)

(*adj.*) unselfish, concerned with the welfare of others

an _____ program to help the poor

2. assent
(ə ′sent)

(*v.*) to express agreement; (*n.*) agreement

forced to _____ to their demands

3. benefactor
(′ben ə fak tər)

(*n.*) one who does good to others

became my _____ in time of need

4. chivalrous
(′shiv əl rəs)

(*adj.*) marked by honor, fairness, courtesy, and courage

praised for this _____ act

5. clemency
(′klem ən sē)

(*n.*) mercy, humaneness; mildness, moderateness

show _____ to first offenders

6. dearth
(dərth)

(*n.*) a lack, scarcity, inadequate supply

a _____ of able assistants

7. diffident
(′dif ə dənt)

(*adj.*) shy, lacking self-confidence

amused by the _____ suitor

8. discrepancy
(dis ′krep ən sē)

(*n.*) a difference; a lack of agreement

a _____ between their stories

9. embark
(em ′bärk)

(*v.*) to go aboard; to make a start

_____ on the long ocean trip

10. facile
(′fas əl)

(*adj.*) easily done or attained; superficial

a _____ writer

11. indomitable
(in ′däm ət ə bəl)

(*adj.*) unconquerable, refusing to yield

admire her _____ courage

12. infallible
(in ′fal ə bəl)

(*adj.*) free from error; absolutely dependable

his _____ judgment

13. plod
(pläd)

(*v.*) to trudge, walk heavily

_____ wearily through the snow

14. pungent
(′pən jənt)

(*adj.*) causing a sharp sensation; stinging, biting

_____ odor of fresh onion soup

15. remiss
(rē ′mis)

(*adj.*) neglectful in performance of one's duty, careless

_____ in doing daily chores

16. repose
(rē ′pōz)

(*v.*) to rest; (*n.*) sleep, relaxation

a much-needed period of _____

17. temerity
(tə 'mer ə tē)

(*n.*) rashness, boldness

have the _____ to answer back

18. truculent
('trək yə lənt)

(*adj.*) fierce and cruel, harsh; aggressive

shocked by his _____ disposition

19. unfeigned
(ən 'fānd)

(*adj.*) sincere, real, without pretense

the _____ emotions of a child

20. virulent
('vir yə lənt)

(*adj.*) extremely poisonous; full of malice, spiteful

a _____ racist

Completing the Sentence

From the words for this unit, choose the one that best completes each of the following sentences. Write the word in the space provided.

1. He is not merely unpleasant but actually dangerous whenever he gets into one of his _____ moods.

2. The pathetic refugees _____ along the dusty road, hoping to reach the Red Cross camp before nightfall.

3. In view of the many able people in public life today, I do not agree that we are suffering from a(n) _____ of capable leaders.

4. His _____ joy when it was announced that I had won the scholarship meant more to me than all the polite congratulation I received.

5. History tells us that many men and women considered "failures" in their own lifetimes were really major _____ of humanity.

6. Humor should be clever and amusing but never so _____ that it hurts the feelings of other people.

7. What good are _____ principles if no real attempt is made to help people by putting them into practice?

8. As soon as the last passenger had _____ , the captain ordered the ship to get underway.

9. As a school cafeteria guard, I would be _____ in my duties if I failed to report any serious disorder.

10. Emphasizing the youth of the convicted man, the defense attorney pleaded for _____ .

11. Do you really think it is _____ to give your seat to a pretty girl when an aged and infirm lady is standing nearby?

12. The brash young lieutenant had the _____ to disregard the expressed orders of his commanding officer.

13. Paula's parents will not _____ to her going to the dance unless she promises faithfully to be home no later than 1:00 A.M.

14. I did not realize how beautiful the child was until she fell asleep and I saw her face in complete _____ .

15. The custom of putting erasers on pencils is one way of recognizing the fact that no one is _____ .

16. Leonard rarely joins in the discussions, not because he lacks information and ideas but rather because he is _____ .

17. Doctors attributed the epidemic to the rampant spread of a particularly _____ strain of influenza virus.

18. Refusing to admit defeat even when things looked completely hopeless, our _____ football team drove 85 yards in the last few minutes to score the winning touchdown.

19. The principal claimed that there were major _____ between what actually happened in the school and the way the incident had been reported on TV.

20. We were all impressed by his _____ use of unusual words and expressions that he had learned only a few hours before.

21. How the _____ smell of burning leaves in autumn arouses memories of happier days!

Synonyms   *From the words for this unit, choose the one that is most nearly **the same** in meaning as each of the following groups of expressions. Write the word on the line provided at the right.*

1. negligent, lax, slack _____

2. leniency, forbearance, gentleness _____

3. timid, bashful; unassertive, withdrawn _____

4. venomous; noxious, baneful; hateful _____

5. brutal, savage, belligerent, vitriolic _____

6. genuine, heartfelt _____

7. unbeatable, invincible, unyielding _____

8. gallant, civil; valiant _____

9. recklessness, foolhardiness; effrontery _____

10. a disagreement, divergence, inconsistency _____

11. to commence, launch, begin; to board _____

12. sharp, spicy, piquant; caustic; racy _____

13. effortless, fluent; assured; specious _____

14. unerring, certain _____

15. to concur, agree, consent, accede _____

16. selfless, rising above personal interests _____

17. an insufficiency, want, paucity _____

18. to lumber, trudge _____

19. sleep; tranquility; a respite _____

20. one who helps others; a patron, humanitarian _____

Antonyms   *From the words for this unit, choose the one that is most nearly **opposite** in meaning to each of the following groups of expressions. Write the word on the line provided at the right.*

1. convergence; agreement, consistency _____

2. scrupulous, dutiful, punctilious _____

3. open to error, imperfect _____

4. a surplus, oversupply, glut, abundance _____

5. to scamper, skip, prance _____

6. a misanthrope; a malefactor _____

7. gentle, mild; meek, unthreatening _____

8. bold, brash, audacious; self-confident, jaunty _____

9. exertion; wakefulness; tumult, bustle, ado _____

10. to disagree, differ, dissent _____

11. innocuous, harmless; benign _____

12. crude, uncouth, churlish, loutish _____

13. selfish, self-centered _____

14. insincere, simulated, phony _____

15. yielding, surrendering, submissive _____

16. harshness, severity, cruelty, inflexibility _____

17. timidity, fearfulness, diffidence, humility _____

18. labored, awkward, halting _____

19. bland, unappetizing, colorless, insipid _____

Choosing the Right Word   *Encircle the **boldface** word that more satisfactorily completes each of the following sentences.*

1. After boasting to me of his family's great wealth, he had the (**clemency, temerity**) to ask me for a loan.

2. By 1781, George Washington's green recruits of a few years earlier had been forged into an (**infallible, indomitable**) army.

3. Lucille is a popular young woman because people realize that her interest in them is sympathetic and (**remiss, unfeigned**).

4. Phil is not too well informed on most matters, but when it comes to big-league baseball, he is all but (**indomitable, infallible**).

5. American Presidents often point to one of their school teachers as the (**discrepancy, benefactor**) who helped shape their character and ideas.

6. I admired his (**remiss, facile**) flow of words, but they failed to convince me that he had practical ideas to help solve our problems.

7. We had no inkling of Calvin's deep-seated aversion to modern pop music until we overheard his (**altruistic, virulent**) comments about punk rock.

8. The lawyer (**plodded, embarked**) through hundreds of pages of the trial record hoping to find some basis for an appeal.

9. In the violent world of today's pro football, good sportsmanship and (**pungent, chivalrous**) behavior still have a place.

10. We soon learned that behind his retiring and (**truculent, diffident**) manner, there was a keen mind and a strong will.

11. As a state legislator, you should not give your (**assent, chivalry**) to any measure unless you truly believe in it.

12. With all the deductions, there is a (**clemency, discrepancy**) of forty dollars between my official salary and my weekly paycheck.

13. Her (**pungent, truculent**) comments during the TV panel show were not only amusing but very much to the point.

14. The planet Earth is a sort of spaceship on which more than four billion of us have (**reposed, embarked**) for a lifelong voyage.

15. In a grim old joke, a man found guilty of murdering his parents appeals for (**clemency, assent**) because he is an orphan.

16. We breathed a sigh of relief when we saw the supposedly missing set of keys (**assenting, reposing**) in the desk drawer.

17. How do you account for the (**clemency, dearth**) of old-fashioned "family doctors" willing to make house calls?

18. Great political leaders know how to appeal to people not only through self-interest but also through their sense of (**temerity, altruism**).

19. You will surely win more support for your view by quiet discussion than by (**chivalrous, truculent**) attacks on your opponents.

20. It would be (**indomitable, remiss**) of me, as editor-in-chief of the school newspaper, not to express appreciation of the help of our faculty advisor.

Definitions

Note carefully the spelling, pronunciation, and definition of each of the following words. Then write the word in the blank space in the illustrative phrase following.

1. accede
(ak 'sēd)

(v.) to yield to; to assume an office or dignity

_____ to their reasonable request

2. brandish
('bran dish)

(v.) to wave or flourish in a menacing fashion

_____ his cane threateningly

3. comprise
(kəm 'rīz)

(v.) to include or contain; to be made up of

a book _____ entirely of essays

4. deft
(deft)

(adj.) skillful, nimble

sew with _____ fingers

5. destitute
('des tə tüt)

(adj.) deprived of the necessities of life; lacking in

aid to _____ families

6. explicit
(ek 'splis it)

(adj.) definite, clearly stated

greatly in need of _____ directions

7. extirpate
('ek stər pāt)

(v.) to tear up by the roots; to destroy totally

_____ all forms of racism

8. inopportune
(in äp ər 'tün)

(adj.) coming at a bad time; not appropriate

arrive at an _____ time for me

9. ironic
(ī 'rän ik)

(adj.) suggesting an incongruity between what might be expected and what actually happens

an _____ twist of fate

10. musty
('məs tē)

(adj.) stale, moldy; out-of-date

a _____ smell in the closet

11. officious
(ə 'fish əs)

(adj.) meddling; excessively forward in offering services or assuming authority

annoyed by the _____ usher

12. ominous
('äm ə nəs)

(adj.) unfavorable, threatening, of bad omen

an _____ report from the doctor

13. pinnacle
('pin ə kəl)

(n.) a high peak or point

reach the _____ of success

14. premeditated
(prē 'med ə tāt id)

(adj., part.) considered beforehand, deliberately planned

guilty of a _____ act of violence

15. rampant
('ram pənt)

(adj.) growing without check, running wild

misled by _____ rumors regarding their whereabouts

42

16. solace
('säl əs)

(*n.*) comfort, relief; (*v.*) to comfort, console

find _____ in music

17. stately
('stāt lē)

(*adj.*) dignified, majestic

impressed by the _____ procession

18. supple
('səp əl)

(*adj.*) bending easily

the sapling's _____ branches

19. suppress
(sə 'pres)

(*v.*) to stop by force, put down

use force to _____ a rebellion

20. venal
('vēn əl)

(*adj.*) open to or marked by bribery or corruption

a _____ official

Completing the Sentence

From the words for this unit, choose the one that best completes each of the following sentences. Write the word in the space provided.

1. A great dancer, like a great athlete, must have a sharp sense of timing and a highly trained, responsive, and _____ body.

2. What a(n) _____ time to ask Milt for help, just when he was having trouble with his own car!

3. The sudden drop in temperature and the unnatural stillness in the air were _____ signs of an unfavorable change in the weather.

4. From 1859 to 1871, "Boss" Tweed controlled New York City through a(n) _____ political machine that fed on graft and extortion.

5. Who would have dreamt that the old attic, with all its darkness, dust, and _____ odor, contained such a treasure!

6. We will never _____ to those selfish and unfair demands.

7. During the darkest hours of defeat, their only _____ was the knowledge that they had fought hard to the very end.

8. Unfortunately, the so-called "recreational facilities" _____ nothing more than a Ping-Pong table and a small-screen TV set.

9. Attacking the present administration, the candidate said that crime has been running _____ in the streets of our city.

10. The unruly mob retreated as the line of deputies moved foward slowly, _____ their riot sticks.

11. Isn't it _____ that he finally inherited all that money at a time when it could no longer help to solve his problems!

12. Even when economic conditions improve, there will still be a large number of _____ families in urgent need of our assistance.

13. It is a truly sobering thought to realize that when one has reached the
_____ of a mountain, there is nowhere to go but down.

14. Who can forget the sight of those _____ "tall ships" with their lofty masts and graceful lines as they sailed past the Statue of Liberty on the Fourth of July?

15. I vowed that I would _____ every weed that dared to show itself in our newly seeded lawn.

16. Whether your act was _____ or the result of carelessness, the fact remains that you have caused great pain to someone who has always been very good to you.

17. Try as we might, we could not _____ our laughter at his clumsy attempts to breakdance to waltz music.

18. The referee showed good judgment in giving a(n) _____ warning that if either team protested his decisions, he would be forced to call a technical foul.

19. I love to watch the _____ movements of little Billy Gomez as he dribbles the ball downcourt and passes off to the taller players.

20. Can I ever forget that _____ clerk in the customs office who insisted that I empty every piece of luggage before him!

Synonyms   From the words for this unit, choose the one that is most
             nearly **the same** in meaning as each of the following
             groups of expressions. Write the word on the line
             provided at the right.

1. distinct, forthright, unambiguous   _____

2. preplanned, rehearsed, calculated   _____

3. widespread, unrestrained, extravagant   _____

4. meddlesome, prying, impertinent   _____

5. dexterous, adroit, proficient   _____

6. ill-timed, inconvenient, inappropriate   _____

7. to soothe, reassure, console, comfort   _____

8. stale, hackneyed, antiquated   _____

9. to swing, shake, flourish   _____

10. flexible, limber, pliable   _____

11. unpropitious, inauspicious, portentous   _____

12. bribable, corruptible; mercenary   _____

13. an apex, acme, summit   _____

44

14. to uproot, eradicate, wipe out _____

15. satiric, sardonic, wry, tongue-in-cheek _____

16. to subdue, crush, stifle, squelch, quash _____

17. to consent, concur, comply _____

18. grand, magnificent, imposing _____

19. wanting, devoid, impoverished _____

20. to compose, constitute, encompass _____

Antonyms From the words for this unit, choose the one that is mos
nearly **opposite** in meaning to each of the following
groups of expressions. Write the word on the line
provided at the right.

1. fresh, sweet-smelling; up-to-date, brand-new _____

2. to provoke, spur, arouse, incite, instigate _____

3. auspicious, propitious, promising _____

4. a low point, nadir _____

5. controlled, restrained, held in check _____

6. timely, convenient, felicitous _____

7. honest, scrupulous, incorruptible _____

8. rich, wealthy; luxurious, bountiful; full, replete _____

9. lowly, humble; servile, abject _____

10. to withhold consent, demur, balk at _____

11. unplanned, spontaneous, impromptu _____

12. vague, ambiguous; implied, implicit _____

13. straightforward, unequivocal, artless _____

14. stiff, rigid; unbending, hidebound _____

15. clumsy, awkward, bungling, inept _____

16. to vex, aggravate, upset _____

17. to implant, sow; to foster, nourish _____

18. to exclude _____

19. reserved, diffident, timid; aloof _____

Choosing the Right Word *Encircle the **boldface** word that more satisfactorily completes each of the following sentences.*

1. He is in for a rude awakening if he thinks that, as the son of a rich family, he will simply (**accede, suppress**) to a position of wealth and power.

2. No doubt there are some dishonest officials, but it is a gross exaggeration to say that graft and corruption are (**rampant, explicit**) in our government.

3. Someone who insists that everyone has a price believes that human beings are (**premeditated, venal**) by nature.

4. Was Oscar Wilde being (**ironic, explicit**) when he said that he could resist everything except temptation?

5. And there was good old Dan, shouting orders, handing out papers, and generally making a(n) (**musty, officious**) nuisance of himself!

6. She may be the daughter of a factory worker, but in that evening gown she has the (**ominous, stately**) bearing of a princess.

7. His idea of debate is to shout at the top of his lungs and (**brandish, comprise**) papers with "all the facts and figures."

8. No matter how ticklish the situation, the hero always devised some (**deft, rampant**) maneuver to avoid capture.

9. Alice felt that she had reached the (**pinnacle, solace**) of fame when the principal of her former school asked for her autograph.

10. The only sure way to (**suppress, brandish**) social unrest is to make possible a decent, secure life for the people.

11. His speech at first seemed highly dramatic and impressive, but we soon realized that he was quite (**destitute, musty**) of new ideas.

12. Vivian has the kind of (**supple, stately**) personality that can easily adapt itself to a wide variety of needs and conditions.

13. They tried to "explain away" their racial slur as a slip of the tongue, but in my opinion it was deliberate and (**premeditated, ominous**).

14. Let's prepare a joint statement that will (**accede, comprise**) the various objections of all civic groups to the freeway plan.

15. Ted and I were prepared for a sharp scolding but not for the (**ominous, inopportune**) silence with which Mr. Fenno greeted us.

16. Coming at a time when I was flat broke, Molly's suggestion that we "have a bite and go to the movies" was highly (**premeditated, inopportune**).

17. Surely you can find some (**solace, pinnacle**) in the knowledge that your father had the love and respect of everyone in this community.

18. I have no patience with the (**musty, stately**) old idea that young women are not "naturally equipped" to study medicine.

19. Even in the concentration camps, some basic feelings of decency and humanity were not completely (**brandished, extirpated**).

20. If the law is intended to limit non-essential use of gasoline and heating oil, it should state this (**explicitly, ironically**).

Analogies *In each of the following, encircle the item that best completes the comparison.*

1. **brandish** is to **sword** as
   a. string is to kite
   b. wave is to flag
   c. inflate is to balloon
   d. board is to airplane

2. **snob** is to **supercilious** as
   a. pauper is to venial
   b. benefactor is to malevolent
   c. thief is to nonchalant
   d. knight is to chivalrous

3. **destitute** is to **wealthy** as
   a. altruistic is to self-centered
   b. scrupulous is to meticulous
   c. supercilious is to energetic
   d. cogent is to clever

4. **invulnerable** is to **wound** as
   a. infallible is to collapse
   b. indomitable is to conquer
   c. inopportune is to risk
   d. insidious is to destroy

5. **solace** is to **grief** as
   a. wound is to bandage
   b. bequeath is to property
   c. repose is to weariness
   d. clemency is to justice

6. **infallible** is to **mistaken** as
   a. ominous is to impervious
   b. explicit is to finite
   c. scrupulous is to remiss
   d. stately is to arrogant

7. **rampant** is to **much** as
   a. opulence is to none
   b. dearth is to much
   c. destitute is to none
   d. negligible is to much

8. **malevolent** is to **unfavorable** as
   a. supple is to favorable
   b. unfeigned is to unfavorable
   c. truculent is to favorable
   d. deft is to unfavorable

9. **pinnacle** is to **high** as
   a. strait is to wide
   b. plateau is to steep
   c. ocean is to shallow
   d. abyss is to deep

10. **extirpate** is to **end** as
    a. suppress is to begin
    b. plod is to end
    c. embark is to begin
    d. comprise is to end

11. **converge** is to **together** as
    a. esteem is to below
    b. disperse is to apart
    c. assent is to above
    d. skulk is to beyond

12. **attainment** is to **achievement** a
    a. panacea is to disease
    b. clemency is to cruelty
    c. temerity is to cowardice
    d. dearth is to scarcity

13. **assent** is to **reject** as
    a. accede is to comply
    b. bequeath is to inherit
    c. ascertain is to scrutinize
    d. expunge is to erase

14. **pungent** is to **odor** as
    a. vivid is to sound
    b. musty is to appearance
    c. unkempt is to feeling
    d. spicy is to taste

15. **cogent** is to **favorable** as
    a. venal is to unfavorable
    b. officious is to favorable
    c. omniscient is to unfavorable
    d. ominous is to favorable

16. **affiliated** is to **unrelated** as
    a. facile is to fortunate
    b. uncanny is to ignorant
    c. explicit is to implied
    d. ironic is to wry

17. **crime** is to **premeditated** as
    a. purpose is to prevented
    b. guilt is to presumed
    c. idea is to preconceived
    d. discrepancy is to prescribed

18. **officious** is to **meddlesome** as
    a. virulent is to harmless
    b. altruistic is to mercenary
    c. stately is to clumsy
    d. diffident is to bashful

19. foster is to **suppress** as
a. repose is to arrest
b. esteem is to loathe
c. comprise is to vanquish
d. brandish is to waver

20. plod is to **quick** as
a. trudge is to heavy
b. sprint is to swift
c. scamper is to slow
d. skip is to light

Spelling   All of the following words, correctly spelled, were introduced in Units 4–6. Underline the word that is **incorrectly** spelled in each of the following groups. Then supply the correct spelling in the space provided.

1. uncanny	atainment	expunge	_____
2. veneal	cogent	bequeath	_____
3. repose	aceed	rampant	_____
4. skulk	benefacter	premeditated	_____
5. acertain	finite	nonchalant	_____
6. malevalent	altruistic	truculent	_____
7. supple	dearth	timerity	_____
8. plod	scrupulous	infallable	_____
9. venal	panacea	indomitible	_____
10. solace	extripate	musty	_____
11. chivalrous	officious	supress	_____
12. esteem	omnicient	virulent	_____
13. inopportune	facile	supercilous	_____
14. comprize	ironic	brandish	_____
15. ominus	pungent	embark	_____

Identification   In each of the following groups, encircle the word that is best defined or suggested by the introductory phrase.

1. earning a degree
a. dearth   b. assent   c. esteem   d. attainment

2. negligent of one's duty
a. diffident   b. remiss   c. omniscient   d. infallible

3. all-purpose remedy
a. panacea   b. pinnacle   c. benefactor   d. clemency

4. smooth-talking
a. cogent   b. ironic   c. facile   d. diffident

5. held in high regard
a. esteem   b. discrepancy   c. temerity   d. pinnacle

6. a shortage of supplies
a. clemency   b. dearth   c. truculence   d. solace

48

7. poor as a church mouse
a. altruistic   b. destitute   c. musty   d. indomitable

8. a generous patron
a. teacher   b. executive   c. counselor   d. benefactor

9. give in to the enemy's demands
a. bequeath   b. accede   c. brandish   d. comprise

10. a rattlesnake's venom
a. venial   b. virulent   c. venal   d. uncanny

11. plain and clear
a. pungent   b. explicit   c. truculent   d. ironic

12. beyond explanation
a. supercilious   b. uncanny   c. omniscient   d. infallible

13. What gall!
a. esteem   b. irony   c. temerity   d. nonchalance

14. showing good breeding
a. venal   b. supercilious   c. chivalrous   d. officious

15. a spot-remover's duty
a. suppress   b. ascertain   c. brandish   d. expunge

16. loiter suspiciously
a. skulk   b. disperse   c. plod   d. expunge

17. conscientious and painstaking
a. rampant   b. venial   c. scrupulous   d. nonchalant

18. drew comfort from the letters of sympathy
a. dearth   b. clemency   c. solace   d. irony

19. rest and relaxation
a. pinnacle   b. repose   c. solace   d. panacea

20. carefully planned
a. premeditated   b. finite   c. uncanny   d. facile

Antonyms In each of the following groups, encircle the word or expression that is most nearly the **opposite** of the first word in **boldface type**.

1. **deft**
a. affiliated
b. invulnerable
c. remiss
d. clumsy

2. **converge**
a. embark
b. assent
c. disperse
d. repose

3. **diffident**
a. mild
b. bold
c. destitute
d. supple

4. **nonchalant**
a. supple
b. embarrassed
c. ominous
d. ironic

5. **venial**
a. incorruptible
b. inexcusable
c. indomitable
d. unbiased

6. **attainment**
a. failure
b. feat
c. repose
d. benefactor

7. **musty**
a. valorous
b. explicit
c. pungent
d. fresh

8. **extirpate**
a. convene
b. imprison
c. prolong
d. implant

R

9. supercilious
a. untimely
b. dormant
c. humble
d. stately

10. ominous
a. indomitable
b. favorable
c. deft
d. diffident

11. inopportune
a. uncanny
b. convenient
c. invulnerable
d. cogent

12. unfeigned
a. pretended
b. lively
c. genuine
d. infallible

13. cogent
a. stately
b. officious
c. explicit
d. unconvincing

14. plod
a. scamper
b. assent
c. esteem
d. ascertain

15. remiss
a. altruistic
b. careless
c. dutiful
d. malevolent

16. omniscient
a. cogent
b. uncanny
c. unfeigned
d. ignorant

17. stately
a. disloyal
b. quiet
c. truculent
d. undignified

18. accede
a. demur
b. brandish
c. suppress
d. bequeath

19. altruistic
a. venial
b. selfish
c. false
d. remiss

20. embark
a. suppress
b. conclude
c. extirpate
d. accede

Completing the Sentence

From the following list of words, choose the one that best completes each of the sentences below. Write the word in the appropriate space.

Group A

cogent	suppress	esteem	expunge
repose	musty	bequeath	diffident
altruistic	panacea	invulnerable	uncanny

1. The judge ordered the court reporter to _____ the witness's prejudicial remarks from the record.

2. You must learn to _____ your urge to make fun of other people if you wish to form lasting friendships.

3. All that he had to _____ to his loved ones was his good name.

4. What this _____ old office needs is fresh air and new ideas.

5. Mrs. Lobel's _____ defense of the school budget convinced many citizens that it should be approved.

Group B

clemency	converge	deft	assent
rampant	discrepancy	brandish	embark
ascertain	finite	disperse	extirpate

1. _____ a heavy stick, he raced toward me while he shouted insults and threats.

2. Delegates from all over the country _____ on the site of the national convention.

3. The mother of the convicted youth pleaded humbly with the judge to show

_____ .

4. Since our attempts to _____ our dog's breed have been
fruitless, we entered her in the "mutt" category.

5. The job of the police is not to _____ the crowd but simply
keep order as long as the people wish to remain.

Word Families

A. *On the line provided, write a **noun form** of each of the following words.*

EXAMPLE: embark — **embarkation**

1. stately _____
2. ironic _____
3. altruistic _____
4. pungent _____
5. ominous _____
6. bequeath _____
7. converge _____
8. disperse _____
9. suppress _____
10. affiliated _____
11. invulnerable _____
12. malevolent _____
13. chivalrous _____
14. nonchalant _____
15. omniscient _____
16. scrupulous _____
17. facile _____
18. virulent _____
19. destitute _____
20. venal _____

B. *On the line provided, write a **verb** related to each of the following words.*

EXAMPLE: attainment — **attain**

1. affiliated _____
2. facile _____
3. premeditated _____
4. unfeigned

51 R

Filling the Blanks

Encircle the pair of words that best complete the meaning of each of the following passages.

1. The school trustees gave up their attempt to _____ the identity of the donor when an intermediary explained that the mysterious _____ wished to remain anonymous.
   - a. comprise . . . affiliation
   - b. accede . . . attainment
   - c. ascertain . . . benefactor
   - d. esteem . . . bequest

2. While it is true that human beings are neither _____ nor _____ , they can certainly use what they do know to avoid making foolish or unnecessary mistakes.
   - a. diffident . . . supercilious
   - b. omniscient . . . infallible
   - c. altruistic . . . malevolent
   - d. indomitable . . . invulnerable

3. Pundits were quick to note the _____ when the councilman, who had campaigned on a reform platform, was discovered to be every bit as _____ as the corrupt bosses he had railed against.
   - a. clemency . . . rampant
   - b. discrepancy . . . venial
   - c. attainment . . . altruistic
   - d. irony . . . venal

4. The senator found some _____ after his electoral defeat in the comforting knowledge that he would now be able to enjoy a life of _____ , far from the strife of the political arena.
   - a. esteem . . . temerity
   - b. solace . . . repose
   - c. panacea . . . dearth
   - d. clemency . . . destitution

5. During the long years that the painter struggled to _____ fame, his talents never failed him. However, once he had actually achieved the public _____ that he sought, they began to desert him.
   - a. attain . . . esteem
   - b. comprise . . . nonchalance
   - c. suppress . . . clemency
   - d. ascertain . . . pinnacle

6. 19th-century hucksters touted their "elixirs" as _____ for every ailment imaginable. Unfortunately, these concoctions often proved more _____ than the maladies they were supposed to cure.
   - a. benefactors . . . musty
   - b. pinnacles . . . ominous
   - c. panaceas . . . virulent
   - d. attainments . . . pungent

7. The salesman pressed me to sign the contract, but I refused to give my _____ to the agreement until all the terms and provisions he so vaguely mentioned were spelled out _____ .
   - a. discrepancy . . . cogently
   - b. esteem . . . officiously
   - c. temerity . . . scrupulously
   - d. assent . . . explicitly

Analogies   *In each of the following, encircle the item that best completes the comparison.*

1. cogent is to force as
a. opulent is to poverty
b. facile is to effort
c. urbane is to modesty
d. pungent is to bite

2. eyes are to scrutinize as
a. fingers are to redress
b. feet are to plod
c. ears are to brandish
d. toes are to muse

3. memory is to expunge as
a. artifice is to deceive
b. gibe is to extol
c. sentence is to delete
d. experiment is to retrogress

4. deft is to adroit as
a. inclement is to balmy
b. punitive is to punishable
c. truculent is to belligerent
d. omniscient is to infallible

5. grimace is to pain as
a. nod is to assent
b. yawn is to exhilaration
c. wink is to nostalgia
d. squint is to nonchalance

6. indomitable is to overcome as
a. infallible is to solace
b. impervious is to penetrate
c. insidious is to coerce
d. invulnerable is to heal

7. scrupulous is to meticulous as
a. stately is to majestic
b. ominous is to auspicious
c. supercilious is to disarming
d. virulent is to diseased

8. pliable is to fold as
a. remiss is to twist
b. unkempt is to comb
c. supple is to bend
d. uncanny is to explain

9. resources are to destitute as
a. plots are to insidious
b. bribes are to venal
c. guises are to incognito
d. relatives are to bereft

10. pinnacle is to loom as
a. attainment is to extend
b. chasm is to gape
c. sojourn is to embark
d. path is to converge

Antonyms   *In each of the following groups, encircle the word or expression that is most nearly the **opposite** of the first word in **boldface type**.*

1. dour
a. genial
b. venal
c. churlish
d. inclement

2. disperse
a. ascertain
b. allot
c. amass
d. alienate

3. stolid
a. unflappable
b. feasible
c. indomitable
d. excitable

4. repose
a. activity
b. guise
c. diffidence
d. lethargy

5. tepid
a. unfeigned
b. ardent
c. supercilious
d. expensive

6. finite
a. uneventful
b. unconscious
c. untidy
d. unlimited

7. demise
a. precedent
b. inception
c. expulsion
d. solace

8. malevolent
a. rampant
b. remiss
c. benevolent
d. insidious

9. negligible
a. officious
b. musty
c. fatal
d. significant

10. invulnerable
a. unprotected
b. uncomfortable
c. unusual
d. unfriendly

11. fallow
a. tempestuous
b. opportune
c. prolific
d. omniscient

12. dearth
a. paucity
b. artifice
c. benefactor
d. glut

13. **duplicity**	15. **holocaust**	17. **explicitly**	19. **esteem**
a. integrity	a. tragedy	a. implicitly	a. extol
b. discrepancy	b. impetus	b. verbatim	b. react
c. jeopardy	c. deluge	c. warily	c. loathe
d. chicanery	d. prosperity	d. expressly	d. plod
14. **suppress**	16. **clemency**	18. **grimace**	20. **facile**
a. embark	a. audacity	a. assent	a. feigned
b. instigate	b. vitality	b. beam	b. premeditated
c. comprise	c. timidity	c. skulk	c. belated
d. stifle	d. rigor	d. wave	d. labored

**Filling
the Blanks**   *Encircle the pair of words that best complete the
meaning of each of the following sentences.*

1. In a(n) _____ gesture of reconciliation reminiscent of the
magnanimous knights of old, Abraham Lincoln declared that the Federal
government would take no _____ or retaliatory measures
against former supporters of the Confederacy.

   a. ironic . . . venial
   b. chivalrous . . . punitive
   c. craven . . . inopportune
   d. altruistic . . . tentative

2. For the umpteenth time the speaker wearily _____ her
reasons for running as an independent candidate who was in no way
_____ any organized political party in this country.

   a. ascertained . . . jeopardized by
   b. augmented . . . alienated from
   c. brandished . . . extirpated from
   d. reiterated . . . affiliated with

3. The famous chef often spoke of his truly prodigious _____
knowledge as a precious heirloom that he wished to _____
somehow to future generations of cooks all over the world.

   a. culinary . . . bequeath
   b. omniscient . . . accede
   c. opulent . . . perpetuate
   d. cursory . . . deploy

4. Though few panaceas work all the time, a trip to the barber is a(n)
_____ remedy for the great _____ of
this world.

   a. indomitable . . . unfeigned
   b. inopportune . . . uncanny
   c. infallible . . . unkempt
   d. invulnerable . . . unpremeditated

5. Most dictators eventually resort to open violence and _____
in their relentless attempts to root out resistance or _____
opposition to their regimes.

   a. nostalgia . . . harass
   b. artifice . . . adulterate
   c. quintessence . . . suppress
   d. coercion . . . extirpate

Definitions	Note carefully the spelling, pronunciation, and definition of each of the following words. Then write the word in the blank space in the illustrative phrase following.
1. abhor (ab ′hôr)	(v.) to regard with horror or loathing; to hate deeply _____ all forms of violence
2. amend (ə ′mend)	(v.) to change in a formal way; to change for the better _____ the club's rules
3. buffet (′bəf ət)	(v.) to slap or cuff; to strike repeatedly; (n.) a slap, blow _____ by high winds
4. chaos (′kā äs)	(n.) great confusion, disorder the _____ brought on by revolution
5. commodious (kə ′mō dē əs)	(adj.) roomy, spacious a _____ pantry
6. corrosive (kə ′rō siv)	(adj.) eating away gradually, acid-like; bitterly sarcastic angered by his _____ humor
7. discern (di ′sərn)	(v.) to see clearly, recognize try to _____ the truth
8. extant (′ek stənt)	(adj.) still existing; not exterminated, destroyed, or lost the oldest _____ specimens of primitive art
9. implicate (′im plə kāt)	(v.) to involve in; to connect with or be related to _____ everyone present in the plot
10. inter (in ′tər)	(v.) to bury _____ those slain in battle
11. martinet (mär tə ′net)	(n.) a strict disciplinarian; a stickler for the rules a stern _____ hated by his troops
12. obviate (′äb vē āt)	(v.) to anticipate and prevent; to remove, dispose of took steps to _____ the difficulties
13. renegade (′ren ə gād)	(n.) one who leaves a group; a deserter, outlaw; (adj.) traitorous; unconventional scorned by all as a _____
14. reprehensible (rep rē ′hen sə bəl)	(adj.) deserving blame or punishment unable to forgive him for this _____ act
15. somber (′säm bər)	(adj.) dark, gloomy; depressed or melancholy in spirit painted in dark, _____ colors

16. squalid
('skwäl id)

(*adj.*) filthy, wretched, debased

forced to live in a _____ tenement

17. turbulent
('tər byə lənt)

(*adj.*) disorderly, riotous, violent; stormy

a _____ mob of angry protesters

18. vociferous
(vō 'sif ə rəs)

(*adj.*) loud and noisy; compelling attention

_____ appeals for aid

19. voluminous
(və 'lü mə nəs)

(*adj.*) of great size; numerous; writing or speaking at great length

bored by those _____ reports

20. waive
(wāv)

(*v.*) to do without, give up

refused to _____ their right to the property

Completing the Sentence

From the words for this unit, choose the one that best completes each of the following sentences. Write the word in the space provided.

1. Although our drill instructor went by the book, he was by no means an overbearing _____ .

2. Shakespeare tells us that "The evil that men do lives after them; the good is oft _____ with their bones."

3. In the chemistry lab, we are taught to handle all _____ substances like potash with great care.

4. The records of the School Board meetings on the proposed bond issue are so _____ that it would take me a week to read them.

5. Who would not feel depressed on entering that _____ old courtroom, with its dim lighting and dark, massive furnishings!

6. One of the signs of maturity is the ability to _____ the difference between things that are secondary and those that are truly important.

7. I didn't expect him to like my proposal, but I was shocked by his bitter and _____ criticism of it.

8. Let me say frankly that I _____ prejudice in anyone, even a member of my own family.

9. Confident that she could present the case effectively to a judge, the lawyer advised her client to _____ his right to a jury trial.

10. A person who has been _____ about by so many dreadful misfortunes will either become stronger or suffer a complete breakdown.

11. We Americans are proud that each change of the national administration, far from being _____ , is carried out in a peaceful and friendly manner.

12. In the museum we can see physical remains of many species of animals that are no longer _____ .

13. We are petitioning the council to _____ its procedures so that all citizens will have a chance to express their opinions.

14. In my innocence, I did not realize that they were "joyriding" in stolen cars, and that I would be _____ in their illegal activities.

15. Are we justified in showing visitors only the most attractive and interesting sections of our cities, towns, or villages while keeping them away from the _____ neighborhoods where so many people live?

16. The trunk of the car was so _____ that it held all of our skiing equipment as well as our other luggage.

17. A person who changes from one political party to another on the basis of honest conviction should not be regarded as a(n) _____ .

18. In our frantic search for the missing papers, we overturned everything in the room, leaving it in complete _____ .

19. The failure to vote in national elections is particularly _____ in the case of young, well-educated people.

20. You can _____ the painful need for offering apologies by not doing anything offensive in the first place.

Synonyms   *From the words for this unit, choose the one that is most nearly **the same** in meaning as each of the following groups of expressions. Write the word on the line provided at the right.*

1. to perceive, detect, distinguish   _____

2. objectionable, blameworthy, culpable; odious   _____

3. to decline, relinquish, forgo   _____

4. tumultuous, unruly, agitated   _____

5. bulky, massive; copious, plentiful   _____

6. clamorous, uproarious, blustering   _____

7. caustic, mordant, acidulous; spiteful   _____

8. a turncoat, defector, heretic   _____

9. melancholy, mournful, dismal, gloomy   _____

10. to batter, sock, thump, pummel   _____

11. dingy, sordid, foul, vile; abject   _____

12. to incriminate, entangle   _____

13. to preclude, forestall, ward off   _____

14. a taskmaster, slavedriver   _____

15. surviving, existing, in existence   _____

16. to detest, despise, abominate   _____

17. comfortable, ample, capacious, roomy   _____

18. to bury, commit to the earth   _____

19. to modify; to improve, correct   _____

20. anarchy, turmoil, pandemonium   _____

Antonyms   *From the words for this unit, choose the one that is most nearly **opposite** in meaning to each of the following groups of expressions. Write the word on the line provided at the right.*

1. cramped, claustrophobic; insufficient   _____

2. extinct, defunct, vanished   _____

3. quiet, soft-spoken; muted, subdued   _____

4. a loyalist, patriot, unswerving adherent   _____

5. bright, sunny; lighthearted, cheerful, jaunty   _____

6. to admire, cherish, respect; to relish   _____

7. neat and clean, spruce; exalted, lofty   _____

8. to claim, accept; to insist on   _____

9. to overlook, be blind to   _____

10. scant, meager; brief, succinct   _____

11. blameless, commendable, meritorious   _____

12. to unearth, exhume   _____

13. calm, placid, tranquil, still   _____

14. order, regularity, tranquillity, peace and quiet   _____

15. to absolve, exculpate, let off the hook   _____

16. bland, mild, benign, amiable   _____

58

Choosing the Right Word

*Encircle the **boldface** word that more satisfactorily completes each of the following sentences.*

1. A compromise agreement reached in the judge's chambers would clearly (**discern, obviate**) the need for a long, costly lawsuit.

2. At lunchtime, the room rang with the (**reprehensible, vociferous**) debates between the Cincinnati and the Cleveland fans.

3. If you examine the evidence carefully, you will soon (**discern, amend**) the contradictions in his story.

4. The Tech team was offside on the play, but since we had thrown them for an eight-yard loss, we (**waived, abhorred**) the five-yard penalty.

5. Some people prefer the (**discernment, turbulence**) of life in a big city to the more placid atmosphere of a small town.

6. Which great poet said that his head was "bloody but unbowed" under the (**buffeting, chaos**) of fate?

7. I wouldn't say that I (**inter, abhor**) housework, but I must admit that I avoid it whenever I can.

8. Even in his old age, Thomas Jefferson kept up a (**voluminous, turbulent**) correspondence with important people in America and abroad.

9. The Founding Fathers set up a method of (**amending, obviating**) the Constitution that is neither too easy nor too difficult to use.

10. Instead of trying to help the people who had elected him, he became involved in a (**squalid, extant**) little quarrel about handing out jobs.

11. The custom by which a young man buys his bride through a payment to her father is still (**commodious, extant**) in some parts of the world.

12. History gives us many examples of how the (**vociferous, corrosive**) effects of religious hatred can weaken the entire social structure.

13. We can expect (**chaos, renegade**) in the years ahead if we do not develop a tough, realistic conservation policy.

14. When he accused me of playing fast and loose with the rules, I lost my temper and called him an officious (**renegade, martinet**).

15. Didn't it occur to them that by signing the letter "Sophomores of Central High," they would (**implicate, waive**) the entire class in the protest?

16. I don't know which was more (**somber, reprehensible**)—making improper use of the money or lying about it later.

17. I'm not so sure that I want to rent a bungalow so (**commodious, squalid**) that we'll have room for guests every weekend.

18. The time has come for us to (**implicate, inter**) our ancient disputes and go forward as a truly united people.

19. It is hard for us to realize that the great men who led our revolution were considered (**renegades, buffets**) by the British king.

20. In 1940, Winston Churchill conveyed to the British people the (**somber, voluminous**) truth that they were fighting for their national existence.

Definitions

Note carefully the spelling, pronunciation, and definition of each of the following words. Then write the word in the blank space in the illustrative phrase following.

1. animosity
(an ə 'mäs ə tē)

(*n.*) strong dislike; bitter hostility

the growing _____ between the rival factions

2. apathy
('ap ə thē)

(*n.*) a lack of feeling, emotion, or interest

greeted my idea with total _____

3. apprehensive
(ap rē 'hen siv)

(*adj.*) fearful or anxious, especially about the future

tried to calm the _____ parents

4. commend
(kə 'mend)

(*v.*) to praise, express approval; to present as worthy of attention; to commit to the care of

_____ her for her excellent grades

5. compatible
(kəm 'pat ə bəl)

(*adj.*) able to get along or work well together; capable of use with some other model or system

statements not _____ with the facts

6. condolence
(kən 'dō ləns)

(*n.*) an expression of sympathy

a _____ call

7. consecrate
('kän sə krāt)

(*v.*) to make sacred, hallow; to set apart for a special purpose

_____ the new church

8. decrepit
(di 'krep it)

(*adj.*) old and feeble

unwilling to ride in a _____ old car

9. deride
(de 'rīd)

(*v.*) to ridicule, laugh at with contempt

_____ our accomplishments

10. ingenuous
(in 'jen yü əs)

(*adj.*) innocent, simple; frank, sincere

take advantage of the _____ youth

11. multifarious
(məl tə 'far ē əs)

(*adj.*) having great variety; numerous and diverse

a busy schedule of _____ activities

12. obsolete
(äb sə 'lēt)

(*adj.*) out of date, no longer in use

get rid of the _____ machinery

13. omnivorous
(äm 'niv ə rəs)

(*adj.*) eating every kind of food; eagerly taking in everything, having a wide variety of tastes

an _____ animal

14. parsimonious
(pär sə 'mō nē əs)

(*adj.*) stingy, miserly

his _____ employer

15. quandary
('kwän drē)

(*n.*) a state of perplexity or doubt

help us out of this _____

16. recalcitrant
(ri 'kal sə trənt)

(*adj.*) stubbornly disobedient, resisting authority

threaten to punish the _____ children

17. reprisal
(ri 'prī zəl)

(*n.*) an injury done in return for injury

fear what they will do in _____

18. revel
('rev əl)

(*v.*) to take great pleasure in; (*n.*) a wild celebration

_____ in all the attention he was being given

19. stultify
('stəl tə fī)

(*v.*) to make ineffective or useless, cripple; to have a dulling effect on

_____ by the oppressive heat

20. suave
(swäv)

(*adj.*) smoothly agreeable or polite

a _____ man-about-town

Completing the Sentence

From the words for this unit, choose the one that best completes each of the following sentences. Write the word in the space provided.

1. I trust you will never have the experience of trying to cross the desert with a(n) _____ mule that wants to remain where it is.

2. The _____ problems facing any President in the last years of the 20th century have made his job one of the most demanding in the world.

3. If you think of all the different kinds of food that human beings are able to consume, you will realize that we are truly a(n) _____ species.

4. It is surprising how often people with very different personalities turn out to be _____ when they get to know one another.

5. This monument, said the speaker, is _____ to the memory of the men who fought and died in defense of their country.

6. If we increase our tariff rates on the goods of other countries, we can be sure that they will raise their own rates in _____ .

7. In totalitarian regimes, censorship and violence are often employed to suppress critics and _____ dissent.

8. It was difficult for us to believe that this _____ and cultured gentleman was a member of a gang of international jewel thieves.

9. Technological advances are so rapid that a particular computer may be "state-of-the-art" one day and _____ the next.

10. Throughout the hot, dusty journey, we _____ in the thought that soon we would be swimming in the cool lake.

11. So there I was, having accepted invitations to two different parties on the same evening. What a(n) _____ to be in!

12. I think that the phrase "on its last legs" is an apt description of that _____ old house down the block.

13. In spite of all the elaborate safety precautions, I couldn't help feeling _____ as she set out for her first sky-diving lesson.

14. Now that I am a senior, it is hard to believe that I was ever as innocent and _____ as the members of the new freshman class.

15. Struggling to overcome his _____ inclinations, he finally reached into his pocket and handed me one thin dime!

16. Simple _____ seems to be the main reason such a large percentage of those eligible to vote fail to cast ballots in any election.

17. From all his growling and snapping, you would think our beagle felt a personal _____ toward every other dog on the block.

18. Don't you think it was in bad taste for you to _____ openly Sam's first inept attempts to dance?

19. The board of directors voted to _____ him for the skill and enthusiasm with which he had managed the charity drive.

20. Although I was unable to visit my old friend's widow in person, I offered my _____ in a heartfelt letter.

Synonyms   *From the words for this unit, choose the one that is most nearly **the same** in meaning as each of the following groups of expressions. Write the word on the line provided at the right.*

1. infirm, broken-down, rickety, dilapidated   _____

2. to devote, dedicate; to sanctify   _____

3. naive, artless, guileless, candid   _____

4. varied, manifold, heterogeneous   _____

5. to praise, give a pat on the back   _____

6. worried, nervous, fretful, jittery   _____

7. retaliation, revenge, retribution   _____

8. commiseration, solace, sympathy   _____

9. sophisticated, urbane, polished   _____

10. indifference, disinterest, detachment   _____

11. frugal, niggardly, penny-pinching, "cheap"   _____

12. to smother, stifle; to neutralize, negate   _____

13. all-devouring, voracious   _____

14. to relish, savor, bask in; to carouse   _____

15. confusion; a dilemma, predicament   _____

16. unruly, obstinate, contrary, ornery   _____

17. enmity, rancor, antipathy   _____

18. outmoded, antiquated, passé, "old hat"   _____

19. to mock, scorn, disparage, jeer at   _____

20. harmonious, in agreement, like-minded   _____

Antonyms   *From the words for this unit, choose the one that is most nearly **opposite** in meaning to each of the following groups of expressions. Write the word on the line given.*

1. generous, openhanded   _____

2. to desecrate, defile, profane, dishonor   _____

3. to praise, extol, acclaim, applaud   _____

4. current, up-to-date, brand-new   _____

5. assured, confident, unworried, certain   _____

6. obedient, docile, cooperative, compliant   _____

7. artful, crafty; worldy, sophisticated   _____

8. mismatched, incongruous; antagonistic   _____

9. vigorous, robust, sturdy, hale and hearty   _____

10. unpolished, crude, clumsy, oafish, loutish   _____

11. homogeneous, uniform, unvaried   _____

12. to arouse, excite, inspire, stimulate   _____

13. affection, fondness, rapport, amity   _____

14. enthusiasm, fervor, ardor; concern   _____

15. to abhor, loathe   _____

Choosing the Right Word *Encircle the **boldface** word that more satisfactorily completes each of the following sentences.*

1. Sue is a(n) (**omnivorous, parsimonious**) reader, with a lively appetite for all types of fiction and nonfiction.

2. The address was so dull and long-winded that it seemed to (**consecrate, stultify**) rather than inspire the audience.

3. Two of the chief strengths of modern American society are the variety and vitality that arise from its (**multifarious, decrepit**) cultures.

4. When Meg appeared with a stack of record albums, we realized that our crash study session might become an all-day (**reprisal, revel**).

5. Your unwillingness to study foreign languages is in no way (**compatible, omnivorous**) with your ambition to get a job in the Foreign Service.

6. I must give you the sad news that correct spelling and good grammar are not, and will never be, (**obsolete, decrepit**).

7. The diplomat was so (**suave, ingenuous**) and self-assured in his manner that we took him for a headwaiter.

8. Yes, there is some (**animosity, apathy**) between different racial and ethnic groups, but it can be overcome by education and experience.

9. Those students who have been doing their work all term need not feel (**apprehensive, recalcitrant**) about the final examination.

10. The handful of (**recalcitrant, parsimonious**) students who refuse to obey study hall regulations are violating the rights of the majority.

11. So we are faced with that old (**quandary, reprisal**)—an income that simply can't be stretched to cover the things that we simply must have.

12. If you can't (**deride, commend**) me for my efforts to help you, at least don't criticize me for not doing everything you want.

13. I think we should offer congratulations, rather than (**revels, condolences**), for the disappearance of that battered old heap you called a car.

14. Her moods seem to go from one extreme to the other—from deepest (**apathy, animosity**) to unlimited enthusiasm.

15. He is so absorbed in himself that he has become (**parsimonious, suave**) in the normal expression of human sympathy and affection.

16. As we begin the third century of our nation's life, we should (**commend, consecrate**) ourselves anew to the ideals of human freedom.

17. Although our society must punish criminals, I don't think we should do so simply as a (**reprisal, quandary**) for the wrongs they have committed.

18. Obviously jealous of Peter's fine talk before the school assembly, Dan tried to (**revel, deride**) him as "the boy orator of East 7th Street."

19. Can you be so (**parsimonious, ingenuous**) that you don't realize she is paying us all those phony compliments to get something out of us?

20. Our Constitution is 200 years old, but far from being (**suave, decrepit**), it is still a vital, dynamic, and highly practical plan of government.

Definitions	Note carefully the spelling, pronunciation, and definition of each of the following words. Then write the word in the blank space in the illustrative phrase following.

1. allocate
('al ə kāt)

(v.) to set apart or designate for a special purpose; to distribute

_____ funds for the project

2. ardent
('är dənt)

(adj.) very enthusiastic, impassioned

the joy of an _____ fisherman

3. assiduous
(ə 'sij ü əs)

(adj.) persistent, attentive, diligent

an _____ student

4. brash
(brash)

(adj.) prone to act in a hasty manner; impudent

a _____ young hothead

5. capricious
(kə 'prish əs)

(adj.) subject to whims or passing fancies

confused by his _____ behavior

6. chastise
(chas 'tīz)

(v.) to inflict physical punishment as a means of correction; to scold severely

_____ the careless employees

7. copious
('kō pē əs)

(adj.) abundant, plentiful

take _____ notes

8. deviate
(v., 'dē vē āt;
n., adj., 'dē vē ət)

(v.) to turn aside; to stray from a norm; (n.) one who departs from a norm; (adj.) differing from a norm

_____ from the original plan

9. emaciated
(i 'mā shē ā tid)

(adj., part.) made unnaturally thin

the starving man's _____ body

10. exult
(eg 'zəlt)

(v.) to rejoice greatly

_____ in their unexpected victory

11. gnarled
(närld)

(adj.) knotted, twisted, lumpy

the _____ limbs of the old oak tree

12. indemnity
(in 'dem nə tē)

(n.) a payment for damage or loss

demand some _____ for his losses

13. inkling
('iŋk liŋ)

(n.) a hint; a vague notion

gave no _____ of how she really felt

14. limpid
('lim pid)

(adj.) clear, transparent; readily understood

the _____ waters of a mountain lake

15. omnipotent
(äm 'nip ə tənt)

(adj.) almighty, having unlimited power or authority

do not want an _____ ruler

16. palatable
('pal ə tə bəl)

(*adj.*) agreeable to the taste or one's sensibilities; suitable for consumption

find the food most _____

17. poignant
('poin yənt)

(*adj.*) deeply affecting, touching; keen or sharp in taste or smell

a _____ death scene

18. rancor
('raŋ kər)

(*n.*) bitter resentment or ill-will

felt no _____ at his defeat

19. sophomoric
(säf ə 'môr ik)

(*adj.*) immature but overconfident; conceited

vexed by their _____ comments

20. spontaneous
(spän 'tā nē əs)

(*adj.*) arising naturally; not planned or engineered in advance

the _____ reaction of a child

Completing the Sentence

From the words for this unit, choose the one that best completes each of the following sentences. Write the word in the space provided.

1. Remembering Fred as a robust 200-pounder, I was shocked to see how _____ he had become during his long illness.

2. _____ is never so bitter as when it arises among people who were once close friends.

3. Aunt Cora arrived with nine pieces of luggage, assorted medical equipment, and _____ supplies of good advice.

4. My travels have shown me that many exotic foods I once considered "disgusting" are really quite _____ .

5. How can you say that the audience's reaction was _____ when the director held up a sign reading "Applause"?

6. When he told me that he was reading *Huckleberry Finn* for the ninth time, realized that he was indeed a(n) _____ admirer of the novel.

7. Somewhere in a(n) _____ pool in the Canadian Rockies is the large trout that will someday grace the wall of my den.

8. If you were as _____ in studying foreign affairs as you are in memorizing batting averages, you would have known how to reply to his comments on the situation in the Middle East.

9. Nothing can arouse _____ memories of long ago and faraway like an old, well-loved song!

10. The teacher decided to _____ a corner of the classroom to an exhibition of student science projects.

11. We were fascinated to see the consummate grace and skill with which the _____ hands of the old carpenter manipulated his tools.

12. Wasn't it rather _____ of Frank to offer the football coach some "advice" on his very first day as a candidate for the team?

13. Some of my friends are mentally rather mature for their age; others are of a decidedly _____ turn of mind.

14. Her casting decisions for the class play are _____ , with no real attempt to select the people best suited for the roles.

15. As the speaker's voice droned on endlessly in the hot, crowded room, I suddenly realized that I hadn't the slightest _____ of what he was saying.

16. The Bible tells us that the Lord will _____ the wicked, but our Student Dean is trying very hard to help Him out.

17. If you wish to recover quickly, you must not _____ in the slightest from the doctor's instructions.

18. Under the American system of separation of powers, no government official or agency can ever become _____ .

19. There can be no _____ for the pain and suffering that your carelessness has caused me!

20. General Grant accepted Lee's surrender with quiet dignity, refusing to _____ over the defeat of a worthy foe.

Synonyms From the words for this unit, choose the one that is most nearly **the same** in meaning as each of the following groups of expressions. Write the word on the line given.

1. ample, profuse, bountiful _____

2. gaunt, withered, shriveled, all skin and bones _____

3. a clue, intimation, suggestion _____

4. edible; appetizing, attractive _____

5. compensation, restitution, reparation _____

6. all-powerful _____

7. unpremeditated, unplanned, impromptu _____

8. heartrending, bittersweet, melancholy _____

9. to diverge, veer, swerve _____

10. lucid, intelligible; transparent, clear _____

11. rash, impetuous; brazen, impertinent   _____

12. knotty, misshapen, contorted   _____

13. industrious, unremitting, sedulous   _____

14. animosity, enmity, bitterness   _____

15. pretentious; superficial, fatuous   _____

16. to assign, allot, apportion   _____

17. to rejoice, revel, glory in   _____

18. to discipline, censure, call on the carpet   _____

19. intense, zealous, fervent, avid   _____

20. impulsive, fickle, unpredictable, mercurial   _____

Antonyms   *From the words for this unit, choose the one that is most nearly **opposite** in meaning to each of the following groups of expressions. Write the word on the line given.*

1. to commend, pat on the back; to reward   _____

2. unaffecting, bland, vapid, insipid; funny   _____

3. clouded, murky; opaque   _____

4. powerless, impotent, feeble, weak   _____

5. smooth, unblemished; straight   _____

6. to conform to, abide by, adhere to   _____

7. inedible; distasteful, disagreeable   _____

8. planned, contrived, premeditated, rehearsed   _____

9. to mope, sulk; to regret, rue, lament   _____

10. mature; judicious, sage; knowledgeable   _____

11. goodwill, harmony, rapport, amity   _____

12. constant, steady, steadfast, unwavering   _____

13. indifferent, stolid, phlegmatic, apathetic   _____

14. plump, fat, obese, corpulent   _____

15. inadequate; meager, scanty, sparse   _____

16. prudent, wary, cautious, circumspect   _____

17. lazy, lackadaisical, shiftless   _____

Choosing the Right Word

*Encircle the **boldface** word that more satisfactorily completes each of the following sentences.*

1. Paul tries to sound well-informed, but his pretentious answers only betray his (**poignant, sophomoric**) knowledge of world affairs.

2. Our meeting last week was marred by a heated debate over how to (**allocate, chastise**) the funds in this year's budget.

3. In the concentration camps, the liberating troops found thousands of victims horribly (**capricious, emaciated**) as the result of starvation diets.

4. Sylvia was (**assiduous, brash**) enough to tell her mother she was going to the dance in spite of the doctor's orders.

5. Since their loud talk and crude manners were anything but (**palatable, limpid**) to me, I decided to travel by myself.

6. Her (**ardent, brash**) interest in ecology shows that she cares deeply about the welfare of this planet.

7. The tastes of the TV audience are so (**gnarled, capricious**) that no one can predict in advance which programs will be successful.

8. Perhaps you have been treated unfairly, but what good will it do to allow your sense of (**indemnity, rancor**) to control your mood and behavior?

9. He seems to feel that it is his mission in life to (**exult, chastise**) all those who fail to live up to his standards.

10. The lecturer explained that the UN is not (**palatable, omnipotent**) and that it can do only what the member states allow it to do.

11. What he lacks in skill, he makes up in (**assiduous, spontaneous**) attention to every last detail and requirement of the job.

12. During depression of the 1930s, the entire nation seemed to take new strength from Roosevelt's (**poignant, copious**) energy and enthusiasm.

13. George Gershwin's early songs gave only a dim (**inkling, deviation**) of the genius that was to express itself in *Porgy and Bess*.

14. After so many years of losing teams, the entire student body (**exulted, gnarled**) when our team finally won the citywide basketball championship.

15. Her simple, (**spontaneous, capricious**) expression of appreciation meant more to me than all the elaborate, carefully phrased tributes I received.

16. The destruction wrought by a nuclear war would be so vast that any form of (**indemnity, inkling**) to the injured would be impossible.

17. We must show understanding and acceptance of those who (**deviate, exult**) somewhat from our own standards of what is "right."

18. Far from being "effortless," her simple, (**limpid, capricious**) writing style is the result of the most painstaking efforts.

19. His weatherbeaten, shaggy, and (**gnarled, assiduous**) appearance did no conceal entirely traces of the handsome boy I had once known.

20. Tennyson speaks of "sorrow's crown of sorrow," by which he means the (**poignant, copious**) experience of remembering happier things.

Analogies   *In each of the following, encircle the item that best completes the comparison.*

1. omnipotent is to **power** as
a. omnivorous is to appetite
b. ominous is to wisdom
c. omniscient is to knowledge
d. omnipresent is to skill

2. thin is to **emaciated** as
a. ingenuous is to dishonest
b. mercenary is to compatible
c. decrepit is to sickly
d. tired is to exhausted

3. suave is to **boorish** as
a. turbulent is to peaceful
b. voluminous is to copious
c. capricious is to brash
d. limpid is to transparent

4. assiduous is to **favorable** as
a. palatable is to unfavorable
b. recalcitrant is to favorable
c. reprehensible is to unfavorable
d. squalid is to favorable

5. palatable is to **taste** as
a. gnarled is to texture
b. vociferous is to appearance
c. commodious is to sound
d. brash is to sight

6. indemnity is to **loss** as
a. condolence is to sympathy
b. reprisal is to injury
c. apathy is to triumph
d. rancor is to spite

7. chastise is to **commend** as
a. deviate is to veer
b. amend is to deride
c. inter is to consecrate
d. abhor is to relish

8. decrepit is to **vigor** as
a. apprehensive is to confidence
b. recalcitrant is to obstinacy
c. parsimonious is to thrift
d. ingenuous is to ignorance

9. stultify is to **stifle** as
a. allocate is to waive
b. obviate is to commend
c. consecrate is to profane
d. implicate is to incriminate

10. ardent is to **apathy** as
a. apprehensive is to anxiety
b. brash is to audacity
c. somber is to levity
d. suave is to polish

11. inkling is to **intimation** as
a. buffet is to quandary
b. condolence is to animosity
c. rancor is to resentment
d. chaos is to indemnity

12. extant is to **extinct** as
a. chaotic is to orderly
b. poignant is to sad
c. spontaneous is to obsolete
d. somber is to corrosive

13. discern is to **perceive** as
a. obviate is to cause
b. waive is to relinquish
c. revel is to annoy
d. buffet is to flounder

14. pool is to **limpid** as
a. explanation is to lucid
b. quandary is to compatible
c. combustion is to spontaneous
d. apathy is to assiduous

15. copious is to **quantity** as
a. multifarious is to duration
b. vociferous is to range
c. commodious is to capacity
d. voluminous is to application

16. vengeful is to **reprisals** as
a. timid is to quandaries
b. contrite is to amends
c. somber is to revels
d. callous is to condolences

17. martinet is to **discipline** as
a. renegade is to loyalty
b. miser is to poverty
c. scholar is to ignorance
d. aesthete is to beauty

18. quandary is to **perplex** as
a. deviation is to conform
b. riddle is to stump
c. dilemma is to solve
d. predicament is to escape

70

19. exult is to triumphant as
a. inter is to vociferous
b. despair is to vanquished
c. spend is to parsimonious
d. obey is to recalcitrant

20. sophomoric is to mature as
a. squalid is to wretched
b. assiduous is to diligent
c. compatible is to agreeable
d. ingenuous is to worldly

Spelling — All of the following words, correctly spelled, were introduced in Units 7–9. Underline the word that is **incorrectly** spelled in each of the following groups. Then supply the correct spelling in the space provided.

1. compatable — martinet — voluminous — _____
2. apathy — somber — indenmity — _____
3. ingenous — consecrate — limpid — _____
4. assiduous — condolense — allocate — _____
5. chastize — obsolete — suave — _____
6. narled — stultify — squalid — _____
7. renegade — poignant — spontanious — _____
8. multifarious — quandry — inter — _____
9. deviate — animosity — capriscious — _____
10. commodious — rancor — corosive — _____
11. disern — omnipotent — deride — _____
12. omniverous — abhor — reprisal — _____
13. implicate — chaos — sofomoric — _____
14. obviate — reprehensable — vociferous — _____
15. revel — pallatable — decrepit — _____

Identification — In each of the following groups, encircle the word that best defined or suggested by the introductory phrase

1. said of an act that is done hastily, without regard for consequences
a. ardent   b. corrosive   c. brash   d. turbulent

2. state of uncertainty or puzzlement
a. condolence   b. apathy   c. rancor   d. quandary

3. feeling of ill-will or resentment
a. indemnity   b. animosity   c. reprisal   d. buffet

4. noisy celebration
a. allocation   b. revel   c. consecration   d. deviate

5. state of complete disorder
a. reprisal   b. waive   c. rancor   d. chaos

6. avoid the necessity for doing something
a. obviate   b. inter   c. chastise   d. discern

7. said of a motor that is difficult to start
a. compatible   b. recalcitrant   c. somber   d. ardent

8. make an addition or improvement
a. allocate   b. inkling   c. reprisal   d. amend

9. economical to the point of stinginess
a. apprehensive   b. suave   c. parsimonious   d. ingenuous

0. out-of-date
a. gnarled   b. reprehensible   c. turbulent   d. obsolete

1. numerous and diverse
a. assiduous   b. multifarious   c. poignant   d. extant

2. an expression of sympathy
a. indemnity   b. reprisal   c. condolence   d. inkling

3. straying from the straight and narrow
a. deviate   b. ingenuous   c. ardent   d. spontaneous

4. seeing eye-to-eye
a. apprehensive   b. somber   c. limpid   d. compatible

5. lay to rest
a. stultify   b. obviate   c. deviate   d. inter

6. on its last legs
a. capricious   b. decrepit   c. gnarled   d. renegade

7. divvy up the chores
a. implicate   b. waive   c. allocate   d. deride

8. on the spur of the moment
a. spontaneous   b. reprehensible   c. extant   d. turbulent

9. all skin and bones
a. suave   b. corrosive   c. emaciated   d. squalid

0. said of a "tearjerker"
a. capricious   b. ingenuous   c. multifarious   d. poignant

Antonyms   *In each of the following groups, encircle the word or expression that is most nearly the* **opposite** *of the first word in* **boldface type**.

1. capricious
a. unselfish
b. steady
c. impulsive
d. limpid

2. deride
a. ridicule
b. discern
c. praise
d. waive

3. squalid
a. decrepit
b. opulent
c. poignant
d. intense

4. apprehensive
a. confident
b. uncertain
c. cautious
d. understanding

5. assiduous
a. compatible
b. lazy
c. somber
d. chaotic

6. copious
a. plentiful
b. squalid
c. in short supply
d. well-planned

7. waive
a. claim
b. reject
c. brandish
d. buffet

8. suave
a. spontaneous
b. multifarious
c. omnipotent
d. crude

72

9. **implicate**	12. **abhor**	15. **animosity**	18. **commend**
a. fold	a. love	a. rancor	a. donate
b. complicate	b. despise	b. derision	b. repair
c. find guilty	c. punish	c. affection	c. separate
d. absolve	d. exult	d. weariness	d. scold
10. **vociferous**	13. **consecrate**	16. **stultify**	19. **extant**
a. convincing	a. obviate	a. excite	a. defunct
b. energetic	b. amend	b. chatter	b. recalcitrant
c. soft-spoken	c. precede	c. inter	c. gnarled
d. eloquent	d. profane	d. cooperate	d. omnipotent
11. **limpid**	14. **commodious**	17. **reprehensible**	20. **ardent**
a. clouded	a. out of tune	a. blameless	a. brash
b. gnarled	b. cramped	b. renegade	b. chaotic
c. emaciated	c. agreeable	c. uncaptured	c. indifferent
d. squalid	d. voluminous	d. implicated	d. turbulent

Completing the Sentence   *From the following list of words, choose the one that best completes each of the sentences below. Write the word in the appropriate space.*

Group A

extant	decrepit	squalid	revel
implicate	obviate	corrosive	sophomoric
martinet	renegade	commodious	discern

1. Her wit was so biting and her criticism so penetrating that a reviewer apt described her book as _____ .
2. In later life he became a _____ whose obsession with rule and regulations became proverbial.
3. Dismissing my answer as pretentious and superficial, the teacher warned me not to vex her with such _____ nonsense again.
4. It was hard for us to believe that this _____ old man was former Olympic hurdling champion.
5. Red Cross officials were appalled by the _____ condition they found in the makeshift refugee camp.

Group B

indemnity	consecrate	amend	quandary
deride	exult	vociferous	waive
inter	chastise	capricious	buffet

1. Our society needs people who will _____ themselves to service of humanity.
2. How long can you expect me to sit by in silence while you continue to _____ things that I admire and respect!

3. The only way out of your _____ is to admit that you were wrong and to do all you can to make up for your faults.

4. We never know what to expect from a person whose moods are so

_____ .

5. Our hopes for financial independence were _____ in the wreckage of the bankrupt firm in which we had invested so heavily.

Word Families

A. On the line provided, write a **noun form** of each of the following words.

EXAMPLE: assiduous—**assiduousness**

1. spontaneous
2. compatible
3. squalid
4. brash
5. consecrate
6. poignant
7. turbulent
8. amend
9. apprehensive
10. discern
11. abhor
12. inter
13. capricious
14. implicate
15. commend
16. chastise
17. deviate
18. exult
19. corrosive

B. On the line provided, write a **verb** related to each of the following words.

EXAMPLE: commodious—**accommodate**

1. corrosive
2. indemnity
3. condolence
4. renegade
5. gnarled

Filling the Blanks

Encircle the pair of words that best complete the meaning of each of the following passages.

1. The soldiers who fell in the engagement were _____ in a portion of the battlefield on which they had fought. The spot where they were laid to rest was not technically "hallowed ground." Still, it was considered appropriate because they had in effect _____ it with their blood.
   a. discerned . . . commended
   b. chastised . . . waived
   c. interred . . . consecrated
   d. implicated . . . buffeted

2. Though I am perfectly willing to give praise where I feel praise is due, I refuse to _____ an action that I consider underhanded and _____ .
   a. abhor . . . extant
   b. commend . . . reprehensible
   c. deride . . . sophomoric
   d. amend . . . apprehensive

3. As the storm increased in intensity, the normally calm waters of the lake became more and more _____ . Strong gusts of wind slapped at our sails, and our tiny craft was _____ about like a Ping-Pong ball in an electric blender.
   a. turbulent . . . buffeted
   b. voluminous . . . deviated
   c. vociferous . . . waived
   d. capricious . . . derided

4. I hoped that my project proposal would be hailed by my classmates with _____ enthusiasm. Instead, it was greeted with "deafening _____ ."
   a. sophomoric . . . indemnity
   b. compatible . . . animosity
   c. vociferous . . . apathy
   d. copious . . . chaos

5. "My years of foreign service have taught me to be as _____ as possible," the veteran diplomat observed, his tongue firmly in his chee "These days, turning up one's nose at another country's national dish, no matter how _____ , might just trigger a very unpleasant international incident."
   a. recalcitrant . . . disingenuous
   b. suave . . . chaotic
   c. compatible . . . squalid
   d. omnivorous . . . unpalatable

6. Infuriated by their treacherous behavior, the enraged party leader severel _____ the _____ who had unexpectedly bolted to the opposition during the crucial vote.
   a. chastised . . . renegades
   b. consecrated . . . deviates
   c. implicated . . . martinets
   d. derided . . . revelers

Analogies

In each of the following, encircle the item that best completes the comparison.

1. **brash** is to **temerity** as
   a. fervent is to apathy
   b. chivalrous is to artifice
   c. hard-hearted is to clemency
   d. ardent is to enthusiasm

2. **omniscient** is to **know** as
   a. omnipotent is to subject
   b. infallible is to think
   c. omnivorous is to eat
   d. invulnerable is to wound

3. **negligible** is to **little** as
   a. bereft is to much
   b. commodious is to little
   c. copious is to much
   d. rampant is to little

4. **shanty** is to **squalid** as
   a. bungalow is to stately
   b. palace is to opulent
   c. cottage is to decrepit
   d. condominium is to obsolete

5. **recalcitrant** is to **mule** as
   a. stolid is to cow
   b. ironic is to weasel
   c. supercilious is to pig
   d. ingenuous is to sheep

6. **somber** is to **mood** as
   a. ambidextrous is to temperament
   b. facile is to effort
   c. vociferous is to noise
   d. dour is to disposition

7. **abhor** is to **esteem** as
   a. attire is to redress
   b. chastise is to commend
   c. delete is to excise
   d. implicate is to suppress

8. **gibes** are to **deride** as
   a. panaceas are to injure
   b. mistakes are to amend
   c. condolences are to solace
   d. attainments are to obviate

9. **corrosive** is to **burn** as
   a. poignant is to pinch
   b. limpid is to bite
   c. cogent is to scratch
   d. pungent is to sting

10. **skinflint** is to **parsimonious** as
    a. busybody is to officious
    b. renegade is to loyal
    c. craven is to emaciated
    d. deviate is to capricious

Antonyms

*In each of the following groups, encircle the item that is most nearly the **opposite** of the first word in **boldface type**.*

1. **chaos**
   a. discrepancy
   b. order
   c. belligerence
   d. anarchy

2. **fortitude**
   a. harassment
   b. intrepidity
   c. benevolence
   d. faintheartedness

3. **turbulent**
   a. peaceful
   b. comfortable
   c. honorable
   d. sensible

4. **assent**
   a. concur
   b. object
   c. coerce
   d. muse

5. **apathy**
   a. spontaneity
   b. demise
   c. enthusiasm
   d. animosity

6. **delete**
   a. expunge
   b. deploy
   c. insert
   d. exhilarate

7. **emaciated**
   a. corpulent
   b. insidious
   c. sophomoric
   d. gaunt

8. **destitute**
   a. averse
   b. replete
   c. boorish
   d. punitive

9. **exult**
   a. revel
   b. degrade
   c. despair
   d. ascertain

10. **impervious**
    a. urbane
    b. porous
    c. extant
    d. assiduous

11. **poignant**
    a. compatible
    b. adroit
    c. obscure
    d. hilarious

12. **pinnacle**
    a. holocaust
    b. acme
    c. nadir
    d. indemnity

76

13. **gnarled**
    a. weathered
    b. cursory
    c. smooth
    d. culinary

14. **tentative**
    a. definite
    b. fallow
    c. rational
    d. finite

15. **rancor**
    a. reprisal
    b. inkling
    c. quintessence
    d. amity

16. **bequeath**
    a. inherit
    b. alienate
    c. endow
    d. allocate

17. **voluminous**
    a. verbatim
    b. brief
    c. lively
    d. wary

18. **meticulous**
    a. tepid
    b. reprehensive
    c. malevolent
    d. careless

19. **palatable**
    a. unkempt
    b. uncanny
    c. uncontrollable
    d. unappetizing

20. **inopportune**
    a. timely
    b. comely
    c. worldly
    d. slovenly

Filling the Blanks

Encircle the pair of words that best complete the meaning of each of the following sentences.

1. In a truly eerie opening scene, the _____ sight of the ghost of Hamlet's father walking on the battlements fills three very superstitious mortals with fear and _____ .
   a. poignant . . . animosity
   b. ominous . . . temerity
   c. somber . . . nostalgia
   d. uncanny . . . apprehension

2. Though I love to _____ in a friend's success, I have never been able to take delight in the discomfiture of a(n) _____ .
   a. revel . . . adversary
   b. accede . . . martinet
   c. converge . . . craven
   d. exult . . . benefactor

3. The _____ old house, a hoary relic of a bygone era, had been closed up for so many years that a(n) _____ odor permeated the atmosphere of every room like an evil yellow fog.
   a. stately . . . tepid
   b. malevolent . . . suave
   c. decrepit . . . musty
   d. squalid . . . limpid

4. It was one of life's little _____ that the implacable judge who had so _____ condemned others to the gallows should himself die by the noose.
   a. quandaries . . . scrupulously
   b. ironies . . . assiduously
   c. discrepancies . . . meticulously
   d. artifices . . . warily

5. In his will, the philanthropist _____ a sizable portion of his great fortune to such _____ endeavors as sheltering the homeless and feeding the hungry.
   a. allocated . . . altruistic
   b. deployed . . . virulent
   c. commended . . . diffident
   d. consecrated . . . obsolete

Unit 10

Definitions

Note carefully the spelling, pronunciation, and definition of each of the following words. Then write the word in the blank space in the illustrative phrase following.

1. acquiesce
(ak wē 'es)

(*v.*) to accept without protest; to agree or submit

_____ to their demands

2. allure
(a 'lür)

(*v.*) to entice, tempt; (*n.*) a strong attraction

_____ with promises of great wealth

3. askew
(ə 'skyü)

(*adj., adv.*) twisted to one side, crooked; disapprovingly

with his tie all _____

4. blithe
(blīth)

(*adj.*) cheerful, lighthearted; casual, unconcerned

the _____ optimism of youth

5. contentious
(kən 'ten shəs)

(*adj.*) quarrelsome, inclined to argue

annoyed by his _____ manner

6. covet
('kəv ət)

(*v.*) to wish for enviously; to desire something belonging to another

_____ his videocassette collection

7. crestfallen
('krest fô lən)

(*adj.*) discouraged, dejected, downcast

comfort the _____ losers

8. disheveled
(di 'shev əld)

(*adj.*) rumpled, mussed; hanging in disorder

always seemed to be untidy and _____

9. exponent
(ek 'spō nənt)

(*n.*) one who advocates, speaks for, or explains

an ardent _____ of modern art

10. garrulous
('gar ə ləs)

(*adj.*) given to much talking, tediously chatty

impatient with the _____ old woman

11. insuperable
(in 'sü pər ə bəl)

(*adj.*) incapable of being overcome

an _____ obstacle to success

12. lamentable
('lam ən tə bəl)

(*adj.*) to be regretted or pitied

victim of a _____ accident

13. misnomer
(mis 'nō mər)

(*n.*) an unsuitable or misapplied name

felt that the title was a _____

14. profess
(prə 'fes)

(*v.*) to affirm openly; to state belief in; to claim, make a pretense of

_____ satisfaction in our work

15. respite
('res pit)

(*n.*) a period of relief and rest

seek _____ from worry

16. retribution
(re tra 'byü shən)

(n.) a repayment; a deserved punishment

suffered _____ for his crimes

17. sinuous
('sin yü əs)

(adj.) winding, having many curves; lithe and flexible

the dancer's _____ movements

18. sonorous
(sə 'nōr əs)

(adj.) full, deep, or rich in sound; impressive in style

soothed by the _____ music

19. vanguard
('van gärd)

(n.) the foremost part of an army; the leading position in any field

be in the _____ of progress

20. wastrel
('wās trəl)

(n.) a wasteful person, spendthrift; a good-for-nothing

the self-destructive life of a _____

Completing the Sentence

From the words for this unit, choose the one that best completes each of the following sentences. Write the word in the space provided.

1. Driving a car along those ___Sinuous___ mountain roads at a height of 10,000 feet calls for stronger nerves than I have.

2. After I heard my new canary sing, I decided that "Melody," the name I had planned for it, was something of a ___misnomer___ .

3. In spite of her rain-soaked clothing and _____ appearance, it seemed to me that she had never looked lovelier.

4. After all my high hopes, I was utterly ___crestfallen___ when the notice arrived that I had failed the driver's test.

5. The ___blithe___ personality that had made her so charming and popular was unaffected by the passage of the years.

6. I confess I suffered a twinge of envy when I learned that my rival had won the prize I had _____ so dearly.

7. He says that he is spending the family fortune "to promote the art of good living," but I consider him no more than a(n) ___wastrel___ .

8. A staunch believer in the equality of the sexes, Susan B. Anthony was one of the most effective _____ of women's rights.

9. Retailers who seek to ___fc___ unwary consumers with false claims should feel the full penalties of the law.

10. Now that the football season has ended, don't you think our athletes deserve a brief ___respite___ before beginning basketball practice?

11. We can all agree that the crime situation in this community is truly _____ , but what are we going to do about it?

12. The body of the slain hero was accompanied to its final resting place by the _____ strains of a funeral march.

13. It isn't likely that the school administration will _____ to your recommendation to do away with all examinations and grades.

14. With the publication of her famous book *Silent Spring*, Rachel Carson moved into the _____ of those seeking to protect our natural environment.

15. You certainly have a right to your opinions, but you have become so _____ that you immediately challenge opinions expressed by anyone else.

16. The pioneers succeeded in settling the West because they refused to admit that any obstacle, however formidable, was _____ .

17. For the innumerable crimes and cruelties he had committed, the tyrant had good reason to fear human, if not divine, _____ .

18. Excessively _____ people don't have the imagination to realize that their endless chatter is boring everyone else.

19. I do not _____ to be heroic, but I hope I have the nerve to stand up for unpopular ideas that I believe are right.

20. If you had listened more carefully to the instructions on operating the sewing machine, the seams would not have gone _____ .

Synonyms   *From the words for this unit, choose the one that is most nearly **the same** in meaning as each of the following groups of expressions. Write the word on the line provided at the right.*

1. argumentative, disputatious, combative   _____

2. untidy, disarranged, tousled, unkempt   _____

3. deplorable, regrettable, distressing   _____

4. recompense, requital, just deserts   _____

5. resonant, resounding; grandiloquent   _____

6. awry, lopsided, cockeyed   _____

7. to assert, declare, proclaim; to purport   _____

8. to yearn for, hunger for, crave   _____

9. despondent, disconsolate   _____

10. a loafer, idler; a squanderer, profligate   _____

11. invincible, insurmountable, indomitable _____

12. temptation, enticement; to beguile, tantalize _____

13. the forefront, cutting edge; trailblazers _____

14. a defender, champion; an interpreter _____

15. twisting, convoluted, serpentine; supple _____

16. an interval, intermission, lull, "breather" _____

17. to comply, accede, consent, yield _____

18. talkative, loquacious _____

19. carefree, nonchalant, happy-go-lucky _____

20. a misnaming, malapropism _____

Antonyms *From the words for this unit, choose the one that is most nearly **opposite** in meaning to each of the following groups of expressions. Write the word on the line provided at the right.*

1. neat, tidy, orderly, well-groomed _____

2. surmountable, conquerable _____

3. elated, cheerful; self-satisfied, cocky _____

4. tinny, reedy, harsh and grating _____

5. direct, straight, unbending; stiff, rigid _____

6. agreeable, amiable, affable; pacific _____

7. to disclaim, disavow, repudiate _____

8. to repel, turn off; a repellant _____

9. a skinflint, tightwad, miser _____

10. the rearguard; stragglers, laggards _____

11. a critic, adversary, faultfinder, detractor _____

12. reticent, mum, taciturn, laconic, reserved _____

13. praiseworthy, commendable, laudable _____

14. straight, symmetrical _____

15. to resist, protest, drag one's heels _____

16. glum, morose, despondent, depressed _____

17. to disdain, scorn, despise _____

Choosing the Right Word   *Encircle the **boldface** word that more satisfactorily completes each of the following sentences.*

1. His willingness to experiment with interesting new ideas clearly put him in the (**vanguard, retribution**) of social reform in his time.

2. The taxi driver was so (**lamentable, garrulous**) during the long trip that it was a relief to return to my lonely hotel room.

3. Since it was the duty of town criers to deliver public proclamations, they were often chosen for their (**sonorous, contentious**) voices.

4. Since Ben was confident he could play varsity ball, he was extremely (**blithe, crestfallen**) when the coach cut him from the squad.

5. Anyone who spends hours, days, and weeks just "hanging around" is a (**wastrel, vanguard**) with the most precious thing we have—*time*.

6. After we had been playing our best rock records for several hours, mother entered the room and begged for some (**respite, allure**).

7. Although we really don't agree with mother's musical tastes, we decided to (**respite, acquiesce**) to her appeal.

8. The poet Shelley, entranced by the joyous song of the skylark, addressed the bird as "(**garrulous, blithe**) spirit."

9. As I watched the gymnastic meet on TV, nothing impressed me more than the incredibly graceful and (**askew, sinuous**) movements of the athletes.

10. The intently longing gaze that he fixed upon my plate told me that Rover (**professed, coveted**) my lunch.

11. Wasteful use of energy at a time when there is a critical shortage of such resources is indeed (**lamentable, sonorous**).

12. (**Crestfallen, Allured**) by the breathtaking views that appeared as we climbed, we struggled our way to the top ledge of Mount Potash.

13. It would be a (**misnomer, respite**) to label as biography a book that is clearly a work of fiction, even though its main character is historical.

14. With present-day hair styles what they are, many men now seem to look somewhat (**disheveled, garrulous**) when they come fresh from the barber.

15. Walking out on the empty stage and speaking the opening lines of the play seemed an (**covetous, insuperable**) difficulty to the young actors.

16. Cy is so (**contentious, sinuous**) that if someone says "Nice day," he'll start a full-scale debate on the weather.

17. When we ended up in the lake, we realized that Ralph was not the expert boatman he (**acquiesced, professed**) to be.

18. The wicked may seem to prosper, but I am convinced that sometime, somehow, in this life or the next, there will be (**exponents, retribution**).

19. With her lipstick smeared, her hair disarranged, and her hat (**askew, crestfallen**), she certainly was a strange sight.

20. A leading (**wastrel, exponent**) of TV's importance in modern life coined the phrase "the medium is the message."

Definitions

Note carefully the spelling, pronunciation, and definition of each of the following words. Then write the word in the blank space in the illustrative phrase following.

1. allude
(ə 'lüd)

(*v.*) to refer to casually or indirectly

_____ to her past successes

2. clairvoyant
(klâr 'voi ənt)

(*adj.*) supernaturally perceptive; (*n.*) one who possesses extrasensory powers

said to possess _____ powers

3. conclusive
(kən 'klü siv)

(*adj.*) serving to settle an issue; final

offered _____ evidence of his guilt

4. disreputable
(dis 'rep yə tə bəl)

(*adj.*) not respectable, not esteemed

unfavorably impressed by their _____ appearance

5. endemic
(en 'dem ik)

(*adj.*) native or confined to a particular region or people

a species _____ to the tropics

6. exemplary
(eg 'zem plə rē)

(*adj.*) worthy of imitation, commendable; serving as a model

improved and became an _____ student

7. fathom
('fath əm)

(*v.*) to understand; get to the bottom of (as a mystery); (*n.*) a measure of depth in water

unable to _____ his purposes

8. guile
(gīl)

(*n.*) treacherous cunning, deceit

the _____ of the legendary serpent

9. integrity
(in 'teg rə tē)

(*n.*) honesty, high moral standards; an unimpaired condition

a person of unquestionable _____

10. itinerary
(ī 'tin ə rer ē)

(*n.*) a route of travel; a record of travel

plan your _____ through Europe

11. misconstrue
(mis kən 'strü)

(*v.*) to interpret wrongly, mistake the meaning of

_____ his motives

12. obnoxious
(äb 'näk shəs)

(*adj.*) highly offensive, arousing strong dislike

angered by his _____ remarks

13. placate
('plā kāt)

(*v.*) to appease, soothe, pacify

tried to _____ my angry friend

14. placid
('plas id)

(*adj.*) calm, peaceful

the _____ water of the lake

15. plagiarism
('plā jə riz əm)

(*n.*) passing off or using as one's own the writings (or other materials) of another person

accuse the author of _____

16. potent
('pōt ənt)

(*adj.*) powerful; highly effective

a _____ force for good

17. pretext
('prē tekst)

(*n.*) a false reason, deceptive excuse

find some _____ for leaving

18. protrude
(prō 'trüd)

(*v.*) to stick out, thrust forth

correct the teeth that _____

19. stark
(stärk)

(*adj., adv.*) harsh, unrelieved, desolate; utterly

shocked by the _____ contrast

20. superficial
(sü pər 'fish əl)

(*adj.*) on or near the surface; concerned with or understanding only what is on the surface, shallow

a _____ anaylsis of the problem

Completing the Sentence

From the words for this unit, choose the one that best completes each of the following sentences. Write the word in the space provided.

1. On the _____ of delivering a package, he sought to gain admission into the apartment.

2. Sherlock Holmes assured Dr. Watson that it was simple deduction, not some _____ faculty, that led him to the document's hiding place.

3. Although the cut on my arm was bleeding quite heavily, it proved to be quite _____ , and only a tight bandage was required.

4. I selected him as my business partner not only because I respect his ability but also because I have unlimited confidence in his character and

_____ .

5. Phyllis was too polite to mention John's crude behavior at the party, but she certainly _____ to it when she spoke of "undesirable elements."

6. By disregarding the flood of excuses, explanations, and justifications, we were able to _____ the true reasons for her actions.

7. When we consider the _____ misery of the last years of his life, we must conclude that he paid in full for all his offenses.

8. The tapes of the conversations were regarded as _____ proof that the official had been aware of the crime.

9. If you allow your foot to _____ into the aisle, someone may trip over it.

10. His skillful use of flattery and "double-talk" to persuade us to agree to his scheme was a typical example of his _____ .

11. Though I was entirely innocent of the infraction of the dress code, the teacher _____ my silence as an admission of guilt.

12. We spent many pleasant hours poring over all kinds of maps and guide books, planning the _____ for our trip across the continent.

13. Too many young people, in an attempt to achieve a casual and "dashing" appearance, succeed only in looking sloppy and _____ .

14. Neither misfortunes nor happy events seem to have the slightest effect on her _____ disposition.

15. Blue jeans, once _____ to the cowboys of the American West, are now a familiar part of the whole world's wardrobe.

16. Their idea of a(n) _____ student is someone so perfect in so many ways that he or she would be too good to exist.

17. The "brilliant" essay for which he received so much lavish praise has been exposed as a skillful act of _____ .

18. America's most _____ weapon in the struggle for world influence is our great tradition of democracy and freedom.

19. It is quite useless to try to _____ "dissatisfied" customers who actually enjoy being angry and making complaints.

20. His conceit and his cold disregard of other people's feelings make him utterly _____ !

Synonyms   *From the words for this unit, choose the one that is most nearly **the same** in meaning as each of the following groups of expressions. Write the word on the line provided at the right.*

1. to misjudge, misinterpret   _____

2. honesty, rectitude, probity; soundness   _____

3. disgraceful, discreditable, shady   _____

4. undisturbed, tranquil, quiet, serene   _____

5. trickery, deceit, duplicity, cunning, chicanery   _____

6. a pretense, cover story; a rationale, evasion   _____

7. decisive, indisputable, convincing; definitive   _____

8. native, indigenous; restricted to _____

9. to grasp, comprehend, figure out, plumb _____

10. mighty, formidable; forcible _____

11. skin-deep, insubstantial; cursory, slapdash _____

12. to hint at, suggest, insinuate, intimate _____

13. sheer, downright; grim, bleak; absolutely _____

14. to satisfy, mollify, allay, conciliate _____

15. insightful, discerning, uncanny; a visionary _____

16. to project, jut out, bulge _____

17. praiseworthy, meritorious, sterling; illustrative _____

18. a route; a schedule, program _____

19. disagreeable, repugnant, hateful, odious _____

20. piracy, theft _____

Antonyms   From the words for this unit, choose the one that is most nearly **opposite** in meaning to each of the following groups of expressions. Write the word on the line provided at the right.

1. deep, profound; thorough, exhaustive _____

2. dishonesty, corruption, turpitude _____

3. weak, inept, feckless; powerless, ineffective _____

4. honest, aboveboard; respectable, creditable _____

5. alien, foreign, extraneous _____

6. candor, artlessness, naivety, plain dealing _____

7. unsettled, up in the air; provisional, indefinite _____

8. to vex, irk, provoke, exasperate, annoy _____

9. bright, cheerful; embellished, ornate _____

10. stormy, agitated, turbulent, tempestuous _____

11. infamous, notorious, scandalous, disreputable _____

12. agreeable, pleasing, engaging, personable _____

13. blind, unseeing, myopic, dense, imperceptive _____

Choosing the Right Word — *Encircle the **boldface** word that more satisfactorily completes each of the following sentences.*

1. The assumption that we can continue to use our natural resources as wastefully as we have in the past is (**disreputable, stark**) madness.

2. In times of crisis, the utmost care must be taken to prevent ordinary military maneuvers from being (**placated, miscontrued**) as hostile acts.

3. Do not be taken in by any (**superficial, conclusive**) resemblances between their half-baked ideas and the sensible program we proposed.

4. For as long as human beings have been able to think they have tried to (**fathom, allude**) the mysteries of the universe.

5. I find no one more (**obnoxious, clairvoyant**) than a person who insists on talking instead of listening to the brilliant and important things I have to say.

6. Instead of (**alluding, protruding**) so often to your own achievements and successes, why not wait for other people to mention them?

7. Mother was as upset as any of us, but she managed to conceal her fears so that she looked positively (**stark, placid**).

8. Of Sybil's ability to divine another person's secrets, it is hard to say where the psychologist leaves off and the (**clairvoyant, itinerary**) begins.

9. It is all very well for science fiction writers to speculate, but is there any (**exemplary, conclusive**) evidence that UFO's exist?

10. A candidate for the highest office in the land should be, above all, a person of unshakable (**guile, integrity**).

11. Phyllis produced a convenient headache as her (**pretext, itinerary**) for having to leave early.

12. Carl maintains that intelligent life must exist elsewhere in the universe, but I firmly believe that it is (**endemic, conclusive**) to Earth.

13. Why not include Mount Vernon in the (**plagiarism, itinerary**) of our spring vacation?

14. If the British government had made a sincere effort to (**misconstrue, placate**) the colonists, would the American Revolution have occurred?

15. Is it any wonder that his parents are worried, knowing that their son is associating with such a (**placid, disreputable**) group of teenagers?

16. In that neighborhood of small homes, a few massive apartment buildings (**pretext, protrude**) like giants set down in a community of dwarfs.

17. Although most of us cannot hope to match her pure idealism, we may regard her noble life as inspiring and (**exemplary, conclusive**).

18. It was clear that her book review was so similar to a review in a newspape that it constituted an outright (**integrity, plagiarism**).

19. Walter's brilliant record as a science major at Cal Tech seems to me a (**stark, potent**) argument for taking four full years of mathematics in high school.

20. Tom Sawyer used (**guile, pretext**) to get the other boys to do his work by convincing them that whitewashing a fence was fun.

Definitions

Note carefully the spelling, pronunciation, and definition of each of the following words. Then write the word in the blank space in the illustrative phrase following.

1. abjure
(ab 'jür)
(*v.*) to renounce, repudiate under oath; to avoid, shun
solemnly _____ his mistaken beliefs

2. acrid
('ak rid)
(*adj.*) harsh in taste or odor; sharp in manner or temper
the _____ stench of burning rubber

3. august
(ô 'gəst)
(*adj.*) majestic, inspiring admiration and respect
the Senator's _____ appearance

4. callous
('ka ləs)
(*adj.*) emotionally hardened, unfeeling
his _____ disregard of my wishes

5. clandestine
(klan 'des tən)
(*adj.*) secret, concealed; underhand
a spy's _____ activities

6. compunction
(kəm 'pəŋk shən)
(*n.*) remorse, regret
felt no _____ for their crimes

7. conflagration
(kän flə 'grā shən)
(*n.*) a large destructive fire
a _____ that left the city in ruins

8. elated
(i 'lā tid)
(*adj., part.*) in high spirits, jubilant; extremely pleased
_____ by their success

9. indelible
(in 'del ə bəl)
(*adj.*) not able to be erased or removed
use _____ ink for the records

10. indulgent
(in 'dəl jənt)
(*adj.*) yielding to the wishes or demands of others
spoiled by his _____ guardian

11. inveterate
(in 'vet ər ət)
(*adj.*) firmly established, long-standing; habitual
an _____ gum chewer

12. irrelevant
(i 'rel ə vənt)
(*adj.*) not to the point, not applicable or pertinent
eliminate all _____ details

13. nocturnal
(näk 'tər nəl)
(*adj.*) of or occurring in the night
listen to the calls of the _____ owl

14. platitude
('plat ə tüd)
(*n.*) a commonplace, stale, or trite remark
bored by a speech filled with _____

15. quell
(kwel)
(*v.*) to subdue, put down forcibly
call out the police to _____ the riot

16. quiescent
(kwī 'es ənt)
(*adj.*) inactive; at rest
a temporarily _____ geyser

88

17. ruminate
('rü mə nāt)

(v.) to meditate, think about at length; to chew the cud

_____ . on the events of his youth

18. tacit
('tas it)

(adj.) unspoken, silent; implied, inferred

have a _____ understanding

19. tangible
('tan jə bəl)

(adj.) capable of being touched; real, concrete

the _____ results of the plan

20. trenchant
('tren chənt)

(adj.) incisive, keen; forceful, effective

impressed by her _____ remarks

Completing the Sentence

From the words for this unit, choose the one that best completes each of the following sentences. Write the word in the space provided.

1. There was no _____ evidence of his sincerity, but somehow we were confident that he would do all he could to help us.

2. Your statement may be correct, but since it has no bearing on the point now under discussion, I must reject it as _____ .

3. Although the disease had been _____ for several years, the doctors warned him that its symptoms could appear again at any time.

4. Though we were angry with each other, we had a(n) _____ agreement to act politely in front of Mother.

5. The fumes released by the volcano were so _____ that they caused great discomfort among people in the nearby villages.

6. How can we possibly accept the testimony of someone who is known to be a(n) _____ liar?

7. If adequate measures are not taken to control a small fire, it may become a raging _____ .

8. The audience seemed to be stirred by the speaker's remarks, but in my opinion they were no more than a series of _____ .

9. Abraham Lincoln's plan for reconstruction simply had the former rebels _____ allegiance to the Confederacy and vow to support the Union.

10. Who wouldn't be _____ at winning that huge prize on the TV quiz show?

11. The debate was decided in our favor when Carole's _____ rebuttal tore the other side's arguments to pieces.

12. His behavior was so rude and offensive that I had no _____ about telling him to leave the house.

13. In the presence of such a(n) _____ assemblage of religious leaders, representing all the major faiths, I felt very humble.

14. She tried to _____ her feeling of panic by assuring herself that there was simply no such thing as a ghost.

15. He is so completely wrapped up in his own concerns that he often seems to be _____ to other people's feelings.

16. The streets seemed safe and familiar during the day, but now we had to face unknown _____ dangers.

17. I have no patience with a(n) _____ parent who gives in to every whim and demand of an undisciplined child.

18. I stretched out under the old maple tree in the backyard and began to _____ on the strange events of that remarkable day.

19. The years of close association with outstanding personalities had left a(n) _____ mark on the students' characters.

20. The documents showed that, years before, the companies had made a(n) _____ agreement to divide the market among them.

Synonyms   From the words for this unit, choose the one that is most nearly **the same** in meaning as each of the following groups of expressions. Write the word on the line provided at the right.

1. overjoyed, jubilant, ecstatic, "tickled pink"   _____

2. persisting, chronic, dyed-in-the-wool   _____

3. to suppress, pacify, squelch, quash, crush   _____

4. a holocaust, wildfire   _____

5. to ponder, reflect, mull over, muse   _____

6. lenient, permissive, tolerant, liberal   _____

7. stately, dignified, exalted, venerable   _____

8. covert, furtive, surreptitious, stealthy   _____

9. nighttime, under cover of darkness   _____

10. insensitive, unsympathetic, thick-skinned   _____

11. still, inert, motionless, dormant, tranquil   _____

12. lasting, permanent; unforgettable   _____

90

13. irritating, stinging, bitter, caustic _____
14. perceptible, actual, evident, palpable _____
15. a scruple, qualm, misgiving, contrition _____
16. penetrating, cutting, telling, acute _____
17. unexpressed, unvoiced, understood, implicit _____
18. to forswear, retract, recant; to abstain from _____
19. a cliché, truism, bromide _____
20. inapplicable, immaterial, beside the point _____

Antonyms From the words for this unit, choose the one that is most nearly **opposite** in meaning to each of the following groups of expressions. Write the word on the line provided at the right.

1. depressed, crestfallen, despondent, "blue" _____
2. sensitive, compassionate, tenderhearted _____
3. open, overt, undisguised, aboveboard _____
4. active, thriving, lively, bustling; volatile _____
5. pertinent, material, apropos, germane _____
6. dull, bland, insipid, vapid, imperceptive _____
7. gentle, soothing, mild _____
8. an epigram, quip, witticism, bon mot _____
9. to affirm, avow, aver, profess _____
10. erasable, impermanent, ephemeral _____
11. strict, severe, inflexible, hard-nosed _____
12. humble, base, mean, lowly, abject _____
13. immaterial, imperceptible, insubstantial _____
14. to incite, provoke, arouse, foment, stir up _____
15. explicit, express, specific _____
16. sporadic, intermittent, occasional _____
17. a deluge, flood _____
18. daytime, diurnal _____
19. shamelessness, insouciance, nonchalance _____

Choosing the Right Word

*Encircle the **boldface** word that more satisfactorily completes each of the following sentences.*

1. It is true that the population of the Soviet Union is slightly larger than our own, but that fact is (**callous, irrelevant**) to the question of military strength.

2. After the Senator's (**trenchant, tacit**) analysis, each of us should have a clear idea of what is involved and where we stand on the issue.

3. Just before going to sleep, we set traps to discourage the (**indelible, nocturnal**) raids of the raccoons on our food supply.

4. In these days of Presidential primaries, candidates can no longer be chosen at (**clandestine, august**) meetings of a few powerful politicians.

5. Your (**ruminations, compunctions**) on the "meaning of life" will be just a waste of time unless they lead to some plans for rational behavior.

6. The deep-seated resentment of the populace, which had been (**quiescent, irrelevant**) for years, suddenly blossomed into open rebellion.

7. The need for careful planning of college applications has been (**indelibly, callously**) impressed on the mind of every senior.

8. George Orwell uses words to express his meaning exactly and vividly, while avoiding meaningless generalities and feeble (**indelibles, platitudes**).

9. Since mother offered no objections, I felt that we had her (**affluent, tacit**) consent to go ahead with our plans for a summer trip to California.

10. Like so many (**clandestine, inveterate**) smokers, she has found that great self-discipline is needed to break the cigarette habit.

11. Millions of Americans were thrilled as they witnessed on TV the simple but (**august, callous**) ceremonies of the Presidential inauguration.

12. Although there was no (**tangible, inveterate**) reason for my alarm, I could not shake off the feeling that something terrible was about to happen.

13. We should not seek to (**quell, elate**) the idealism and enthusiasm of youth, but rather to direct those impulses into useful channels.

14. When we asked him to contribute to the charity drive, he dismissed us with the (**acrid, indulgent**) remark, "Not interested."

15. The superpowers intervened to prevent the brushfire war from engulfing the entire region in a full-scale (**conflagration, compunction**).

16. As part of the settlement, the company must henceforth (**ruminate, abjure**) unsubstantiated claims for its product.

17. Because her misconduct was clearly deliberate, we have no feelings of (**compunction, platitude**) in sentencing her to ten days of detention.

18. Taking third place in the hundred-meter dash in the intramural track meet left me satisfied but scarcely (**callous, elated**).

19. Judge Burnham has a reputation for being (**indulgent, tacit**)—but not when confronting a teenager charged with reckless driving.

20. We may criticize Americans for many things, but they are never (**elated, callous**) when appeals for help come from distressed people.

Analogies *In each of the following, encircle the item that best completes the comparison.*

1. **conflagration** is to **brush fire** as
a. blizzard is to avalanche
b. deluge is to monsoon
c. tornado is to drought
d. hurricane is to shower

2. **blithe** is to **glum** as
a. garrulous is to talkative
b. pertinent is to irrelevant
c. august is to clandestine
d. sinuous is to quiescent

3. **indelible** is to **erase** as
a. insuperable is to conquer
b. indulgent is to pamper
c. inveterate is to refine
d. unfathomable is to misconstrue

4. **acrid** is to **smell** as
a. disheveled is to hear
b. tacit is to see
c. callous is to taste
d. tangible is to touch

5. **quell** is to **quash** as
a. covet is to shun
b. fathom is to dive
c. acquiesce is to comply
d. protrude is to abjure

6. **miser** is to **amass** as
a. exponent is to allude
b. vanguard is to conclude
c. wastrel is to squander
d. dent is to protrude

7. **placate** is to **provoke** as
a. profess is to avow
b. profess is to disclaim
c. profess is to lament
d. profess is to allure

8. **exponent** is to **pro** as
a. advocate is to con
b. opponent is to pro
c. adversary is to con
d. critic is to pro

9. **august** is to **abject** as
a. callous is to insensitive
b. placid is to tempestuous
c. tacit is to verbatim
d. clandestine is to furtive

10. **sonorous** is to **sound** as
a. august is to season
b. aromatic is to smell
c. sinuous is to taste
d. callous is to touch

11. **guile** is to **unfavorable** as
a. integrity is to favorable
b. clairvoyance is to unfavorable
c. plagiarism is to favorable
d. itinerary is to unfavorable

12. **superficial** is to **trenchant** as
a. vivid is to askew
b. stark is to tepid
c. weak is to potent
d. decisive is to conclusive

13. **exemplary** is to **favorable** as
a. disreputable is to unfavorable
b. obnoxious is to favorable
c. august is to unfavorable
d. garrulous is to favorable

14. **clandestine** is to **secret** as
a. lamentable is to commendable
b. indulgent is to permissive
c. contentious is to harmonious
d. endemic is to tacit

15. **fathom** is to **depth** as
a. width is to meter
b. bushel is to height
c. knot is to speed
d. inch is to yard

16. **platitude** is to **banal** as
a. respite is to arduous
b. pretext is to contentious
c. misnomer is to erroneous
d. vanguard is to tacit

17. **clairvoyant** is to **insight** as
a. potent is to power
b. garrulous is to silence
c. callous is to sympathy
d. indulgent is to harshness

18. **impostor** is to **guile** as
a. swindler is to integrity
b. peacemaker is to contentious
c. wastrel is to thrift
d. siren is to allure

9. crestfallen is to **down** as
a. lamentable is to up
b. blithe is to down
c. elated is to up
d. nocturnal is to down

20. cow is to **ruminate** as
a. mammal is to mole
b. rodent is to gnaw
c. amphibian is to fly
d. reptile is to hibernate

Spelling   *All of the following words, correctly spelled, were introduced in Units 10–12. Underline the word that is incorrectly spelled in each of the following groups. Then supply the correct spelling in the space provided.*

1. guile	lamentable	misconstrew	_____
2. aquiesce	inveterate	retribution	_____
3. nocternal	disheveled	wastrel	_____
4. clarvoyant	askew	itinerary	_____
5. pretext	sinuous	alure	_____
6. plaigarism	exemplary	ruminate	_____
7. irrelevant	respit	callous	_____
8. compunction	indelable	placate	_____
9. fathom	conflagration	quel	_____
10. placid	disreputable	vangard	_____
11. exponent	garulous	contentious	_____
12. protrude	blithe	quiesent	_____
13. superficial	misnomer	alude	_____
14. insuperible	platitude	potent	_____
15. endemic	sonerous	integrity	_____

Identification   *In each of the following groups, encircle the word that is best defined or suggested by the introductory phrase.*

1. put down a disturbance
a. allure   b. ruminate   c. acquiesce   d. quell

2. blessed with second sight
a. crestfallen   b. clairvoyant   c. nocturnal   d. trenchant

3. "The early bird gets the worm."
a. compunction   b. platitude   c. allure   d. respite

4. dyed-in-the-wool
a. callous   b. stark   c. disheveled   d. inveterate

5. spends like there's no tomorrow
a. integrity   b. guile   c. wastrel   d. itinerary

6. ears that stand out conspicuously
a. protrude   b. placate   c. abjure   d. allude

7. a sense of guilt or uncertainty about some action
a. compunction   b. retribution   c. vanguard   d. guile

8. the fire that destroyed Chicago in 1871
a. wastrel   b. conflagration   c. nocturnal   d. allure

9. make an indirect reference to your athletic achievements
a. plagiarize   b. acquiesce   c. misconstrue   d. allude

10. get to the bottom of the situation
a. protrude   b. fathom   c. quell   d. covet

11. an eye for an eye
a. pretext   b. clairvoyant   c. retribution   d. plagiarism

12. said of a chatterbox
a. garrulous   b. lamentable   c. alluring   d. sonorous

13. happy-go-lucky
a. blithe   b. contentious   c. sinuous   d. superficial

14. "I take it all back."
a. covet   b. ruminate   c. profess   d. abjure

15. artists experimenting in new forms and techniques
a. platitude   b. vanguard   c. itinerary   d. starkness

16. a cover story
a. plagiarism   b. pretext   c. retribution   d. irrelevancy

17. an awe-inspiring religious ceremony
a. crestfallen   b. trenchant   c. elated   d. august

18. language that makes its point with force and penetration
a. indelible   b. trenchant   c. blithe   d. sinuous

19. a time-out in a hotly contested basketball game
a. respite   b. misnomer   c. pretext   d. wastrel

20. a style that is simple, unadorned, harsh
a. placid   b. nocturnal   c. stark   d. tangible

Antonyms   *In each of the following groups, encircle the word or expression that is most nearly the **opposite** of the wo in **boldface type**.*

1. allure
a. discover
b. accept
c. repel
d. escape

2. contentious
a. difficult
b. twisted
c. small
d. agreeable

3. potent
a. edible
b. repeated
c. tasty
d. ineffective

4. lamentable
a. praiseworthy
b. unfortunate
c. carefree
d. honest

5. guile
a. affluence
b. frankness
c. fraud
d. sweetness

6. tacit
a. cheap
b. expressed
c. undamaged
d. talkative

7. inveterate
a. foolish
b. closed
c. ungainly
d. occasional

8. crestfallen
a. brave
b. disappointe
c. neat
d. joyful

9. endemic
a. native
b. healthy
c. alien
d. superficial

10. placate
a. destroy
b. vex
c. calm
d. enlarge

11. disreputable
a. angry
b. respected
c. organized
d. extreme

12. irrelevant
a. concerned
b. prompt
c. appropriate
d. ugly

13. callous
a. sensitive
b. hidden
c. tight
d. curved

14. conclusive
a. contentious
b. final
c. doubtful
d. important

15. covet
a. release
b. hide
c. disdain
d. desire

16. quiescent
a. deafening
b. inactive
c. bustling
d. certain

17. acrid
a. sweet
b. sour
c. new
d. strong

18. indelible
a. temporary
b. sad
c. forceful
d. certain

19. placid
a. disturbed
b. natural
c. steep
d. rich

20. sinuous
a. straight
b. curved
c. clean
d. open

Completing the Sentence	*From the following list of words choose the one that best completes each of the sentences below. Write the word in the appropriate space.*

Group A

allude	itinerary	lamentable	stark
misconstrue	fathom	inveterate	clandestine
respite	disreputable	garrulous	plagiarize

1. The _____ of Bill's tour was carefully planned to enable him to play at top-ranking golf courses from coast to coast.

2. He is such a(n) _____ bridge player that he once tried to set up a game during a subway ride.

3. She wore only a single strand of pearls to set off the _____ simplicity of her black dress.

4. Although the bus driver had a rather _____ appearance, we found that he was courteous and dependable all during the journey.

5. I have an uncomfortable feeling that the hosts of late-night talk shows are _____ each other's jokes.

Group B

profess	retribution	protrude	exemplary
wastrel	placate	exponent	vanguard
tangible	pretext	contentious	elate

1. Since he has little interest in books, I suspect that his frequent trips to the library are no more than a(n) _____ to meet girls.

2. That brilliant program on urban problems has placed her firmly in the _____ of producers of TV documentaries.

3. Although he _____ to have no interest in money, I notice that he is very careful about collecting every dollar due him.

4. The police know the suspect's identity but have so far failed to uncover _____ evidence linking him to the crime.

5. When I finally understood why my sister was angry with me, I did all I could to _____ her.

Word Families

A. *On the line provided, write a* **noun form** *of each of the following words.*
EXAMPLE: tangible—**tangibility**

1. indulgent _____
2. placid _____
3. profess _____
4. protrude _____
5. lamentable _____
6. sinuous _____
7. allude _____
8. potent _____
9. conclusive _____
10. clairvoyant _____
11. ruminate _____
12. contentious _____
13. sonorous _____
14. exemplary _____
15. superficial _____
16. elated _____
17. irrelevant _____
18. quiescent _____

B. *On the line provided, write a* **verb** *related to each of the following words.*
EXAMPLE: conclusive—**conclude**

1. wastrel _____
2. indulgent _____
3. contentious _____
4. plagiarism _____
5. lamentable _____

Filling the Blanks   *Encircle the pair of words that best complete each of the following passages.*

1. Utterly _____ at their upset defeat, the Belleville squad looked on dismally as the trophy they had so much _____ was awarded to their archrivals from Henderson.
   a. lamentable . . . abjured
   b. crestfallen . . . coveted
   c. disheveled . . . ruminated
   d. blithe . . . professed

2. High winds fanned the flames, and in no time at all the _____ had spread to a nearby tire factory. Clouds of thick black smoke billowed up into the sky, and the _____ stench of burning rubber filled the air.
   a. contention . . . obnoxious
   b. retribution . . . indelible
   c. compunction . . . potent
   d. conflagration . . . acrid

3. After romping around with my six-year-old nephew all afternoon, I had become woefully _____ . My trousers were rumpled, my shirttails were hanging out, and my tie was all _____ .
   a. disheveled . . . askew
   b. disreputable . . . crestfallen
   c. garrulous . . . acrid
   d. lamentable . . . sinuous

4. I had hoped that the candidates would make a few _____ observations during the course of the debate. All I got, however, were the same tired old _____ that politicians have been mouthing for decades.
   a. irrelevant . . . plagiarisms
   b. exemplary . . . pretexts
   c. trenchant . . . platitudes
   d. superficial . . . ruminations

5. During the evening, Ned must have _____ to his close acquaintance with at least a dozen celebrities. Afterward, we all agreed that his nickname, "Namedropper Ned," was no _____ .
   a. protruded . . . plagiarism
   b. alluded . . . misnomer
   c. misconstrued . . . pretext
   d. protruded . . . platitude

6. The trail nicknamed "Dead Man's Curves" is so steep and _____ that even the most proficient and experienced skiers often must stop for a brief _____ before completing the course.
   a. sinuous . . . respite
   b. disreputable . . . pretext
   c. stark . . . itinerary
   d. clandestine . . . compunction

7. In view of the countless crimes the dictator had committed while in power, the revolutionary tribunal expressed no _____ in seeking the sternest _____ on behalf of the people.
   a. guile . . . conflagration
   b. integrity . . . respite
   c. compunction . . . retribution
   d. pretext . . . vanguard

Analogies   *In each of the following, encircle the item that best completes the comparison.*

1. insuperable is to **overcome** as
a. infallible is to explain
b. omnivorous is to eat
c. indomitable is to tame
d. feasible is to do

2. ruminate is to **muse** as
a. quell is to suppress
b. covet is to abhor
c. brandish is to waive
d. profess is to abjure

3. hair is to **unkempt** as
a. room is to musty
b. odor is to pungent
c. trunk is to commodious
d. clothing is to disheveled

4. crestfallen is to **exult** as
a. slow is to plod
b. elated is to lament
c. brash is to revel
d. apprehensive is to tremble

5. indelible is to **expunge** as
a. omniscient is to know
b. impervious is to pierce
c. omnipotent is to rule
d. invulnerable is to cure

6. explicit is to **tacit** as
a. spontaneous is to premeditated
b. suave is to urbane
c. tepid is to acrid
d. poignant is to ingenuous

7. tangible is to **touch** as
a. lamentable is to rejoice
b. amicable is to hinder
c. pliable is to bend
d. feasible is to avoid

8. trenchant is to **cut** as
a. ardent is to flow
b. sinuous is to scar
c. garrulous is to silence
d. corrosive is to burn

9. quiescent is to **repose** as
a. askew is to activity
b. turbulent is to motion
c. scrupulous is to speed
d. negligible is to significance

10. holocaust is to **conflagration** as
a. deluge is to inundation
b. famine is to plague
c. chaos is to revolution
d. earthquake is to avalanche

11. integrity is to **duplicity** as
a. clemency is to mercy
b. animosity is to rancor
c. chivalry is to gallantry
d. candor is to guile

12. disreputable is to **esteem** as
a. exemplary is to extol
b. reprehensible is to commend
c. unjust is to redress
d. ludicrous is to deride

13. covet is to **craving** as
a. abhor is to aversion
b. scrutinize is to apathy
c. esteem is to animosity
d. discern is to antagonism

14. callous is to **sensitivity** as
a. facile is to skill
b. clairvoyant is to discernment
c. stolid is to emotion
d. belligerent is to hostility

15. placid is to **tranquillity** as
a. fainthearted is to fortitude
b. diffident is to audacity
c. nonchalant is to concern
d. limpid is to clarity

16. tentative is to **conclusive** as
a. dour is to obnoxious
b. august is to destitute
c. cursory is to meticulous
d. stark is to austere

17. decor is to **opulent** as
a. sound is to sonorous
b. duty is to officious
c. discrepancy is to irrelevant
d. habit is to inveterate

18. truculent is to **contentious** as
a. craven is to intrepid
b. adroit is to deft
c. clandestine is to nocturnal
d. malevolent is to benevolent

19. potent is to **clout** as
a. voluminous is to brevity
b. tepid is to heat
c. squalid is to allure
d. cogent is to force

20. field is to **fallow** as
a. weather is to inclement
b. root is to gnarled
c. building is to decrepit
d. volcano is to dormant

21. backbone is to **fortitude** as
a. stomach is to altruism
b. cheek is to temerity
c. lip is to diffidence
d. spine is to adversity

22. hands are to **ambidextrous** as
a. adversaries are to amicable
b. moods are to ironic
c. languages are to bilingual
d. duties are to insidious

Antonyms   *In each of the following groups, encircle the word that is most nearly the* **opposite** *of the first word in* **boldface type**.

1. acquiesce
a. cancel
b. deploy
c. protest
d. accede

2. venal
a. unstoppable
b. unbribable
c. unforgivable
d. unpredictable

3. askew
a. symmetrical
b. voluminous
c. sinuous
d. haggard

4. bereft
a. endemic
b. devoid
c. assiduous
d. replete

5. blithe
a. jaunty
b. venial
c. despondent
d. capricious

6. inter
a. placate
b. exhume
c. skulk
d. depart

7. garrulous
a. ironic
b. ambidextrous
c. voluble
d. taciturn

8. scrupulous
a. remiss
b. palatable
c. averse
d. virulent

9. exponent
a. retribution
b. martinet
c. adversary
d. compunction

10. benevolent
a. obsolete
b. malicious
c. rampant
d. arduous

11. indulgent
a. strict
b. hungry
c. poignant
d. doting

12. chastise
a. coerce
b. comprise
c. converge
d. commend

13. misconstrue
a. understand
b. quote
c. reiterate
d. scrutinize

14. discrepancy
a. platitude
b. quintessence
c. consistency
d. artifice

15. abjure
a. redress
b. reaffirm
c. recall
d. relieve

16. belligerent
a. uncanny
b. apathetic
c. conciliatory
d. affiliated

17. august
a. altruistic
b. stately
c. compatible
d. base

18. recalcitrant
a. amenable
b. multifarious
c. renegade
d. corpulent

19. clandestine
a. extant
b. overt
c. harassed
d. expensive

20. supple
a. emaciated
b. graceful
c. exhilarated
d. stiff

21. stark
a. inopportune
b. intimated
c. ornate
d. perpetual

22. alienate
a. reconcile
b. gape
c. stultify
d. estrange

23. somber
a. copious
b. bright
c. finite
d. dingy

24. misnomer
a. bon mot
b. rive gauche
c. mot juste
d. beau idéal

100

Filling the Blanks

Encircle the pair of words that best complete the meaning of each of the following sentences.

1. Though the _____ of our summer tour does include a brief _____ in Paris, where we will stay at the world's most luxurious hotel, we will spend most of the trip exploring various points of interest in the south of France.
   a. vanguard . . . demise
   b. itinerary . . . sojourn
   c. quandary . . . respite
   d. indemnity . . . dearth

2. At first glance the painting bears a(n) _____ resemblance to something by Rembrandt, but on closer inspection the eye begins to _____ subtle differences in style and technique that show it to be the work of another painter.
   a. insidious . . . ascertain
   b. unfeigned . . . amend
   c. superficial . . . discern
   d. ominous . . . fathom

3. Though he _____ to be learned and refined, his ideas and attitudes show his mind to be woefully _____ and uncouth.
   a. professes . . . sophomoric
   b. assents . . . urbane
   c. abhors . . . suave
   d. alludes . . . supercilious

4. When the noise of his uncle's drunken_____ interrupts the quiet of the night, Prince Hamlet remarks that such _____ carousing is, to his mind, "a custom more honored in the breach than in the observance."
   a. nostalgia . . . culinary
   b. indulgence . . . clandestine
   c. solace . . . vociferous
   d. revelry . . . nocturnal

5. Though the vision of "striking it rich overnight" held such an irresistible _____ for poor Americans in 1849, most of those who were attracted to the goldfields of California ended up as _____ as they had started out.
   a. guise . . . parsimonious
   b. impetus . . . blithe
   c. allure . . . destitute
   d. pretext . . . bereft

6. I had always admired the ease and _____ with which he turned out essays and articles so effortlessly until one day I discovered that he had actually _____ three-quarters of what he claimed to be his own work.
   a. duplicity . . . retrogressed
   b. facility . . . plagiarized
   c. temerity . . . alienated
   d. diffidence . . . adulterated

Definitions

Note carefully the spelling, pronunciation, and definition of each of the following words. Then write the word in the blank space in the illustrative phrase following.

1. antipathy
(an 'tip ə thē)

(*n.*) a strong dislike, hostile feeling

has an _____ for spinach

2. applicable
('ap lə kə bəl)

(*adj.*) capable of being applied; relevant, suitable

not _____ to this case

3. asset
('as et)

(*n.*) something of value; a resource; an advantage

the company's _____

4. beset
(bē 'set)

(*v.*) to attack from all sides; to surround, hem in; (*part.*) harassed, troubled

_____ with many fears

5. compassion
(kəm 'pash ən)

(*n.*) sympathy for another's suffering; pity

felt _____ for the poor

6. decorum
(di 'kôr əm)

(*n.*) proper behavior, good taste; orderliness

disturb the _____ of the meeting

7. duress
(dù 'res)

(*n.*) compulsion by threat; forcible confinement

confessed under _____

8. exuberant
(eg 'zü bər ənt)

(*adj.*) high-spirited, enthusiastic, unrestrained; excessive, abundant

unable to control their _____ spirits

9. facsimile
(fak 'sim ə lē)

(*n.*) an exact copy

obtain a _____ of the Constitution

10. imbibe
(im 'bīb)

(*v.*) to drink; to take in, absorb

_____ knowledge from many sources

11. implacable
(im 'plak ə bəl)

(*adj.*) not to be satisfied or pacified; unyielding

fighting against an _____ enemy

12. infinitesimal
(in fin ə 'tes ə məl)

(*adj.*) so small as to be almost immeasurable; minute

an _____ amount of dust

13. innocuous
(i 'näk yü əs)

(*adj.*) harmless, inoffensive; insignificant

makes _____ remarks

14. militate
('mil ə tāt)

(*n.*) to have effect or force on or against someone or something

since the present situation _____ against the success of the undertaking

15. patent
('pat ənt)

(n.) exclusive rights over an invention; (v.) to arrange or obtain such rights; (adj.) plain, open to view

make a _____ error

16. prowess
('praù əs)

(n.) distinguished bravery; superior skill or ability

won fame for his military _____

17. sedate
(sə 'dāt)

(adj.) quiet, settled, sober; (v.) to administer a tranquilizer

conduct herself in a _____ manner

18. stentorian
(sten 'tôr ē ən)

(adj.) extremely loud

the speaker's _____ delivery

19. stipulate
('stip yə lāt)

(v.) to arrange specifically; to require as a condition of agreement

_____ the terms of employment

20. ultimatum
(əl tə 'mā təm)

(n.) a final proposal or statement of conditions

present an _____ to the enemy

Completing the Sentence

From the words for this unit, choose the one that best completes each of the following sentences. Write the word in the space provided.

1. The player's chronic shoulder injury _____ against the idea of extending his baseball career for another season.

2. The landlord's _____ was simple and direct: Pay the rent increase or get out.

3. I am well on the road to becoming a millionaire because I have just been awarded the _____ for an automatic homework machine.

4. How can you expect her to concern herself with your problems when she is so _____ with troubles of her own!

5. I must admit that I feel a strong _____ toward anyone whose table manners are as bad as Sid's.

6. I was amazed to see how a few years had transformed an unruly tomboy into a well-bred, _____ young lady.

7. Dr. Albert Schweitzer had not only great scientific ability but a deep sense of _____ for suffering humanity.

8. American law forbids a suspect to be arrested and held in any form of _____ without being formally charged.

9. He has his shortcomings, but as compared with his great services to his community and nation, they seem all but _____ .

10. His chief _____ both in business and in social life are his excellent appearance and pleasant manner.

11. The artist's latest work acclaimed by the critics seemed to me to be no more than a(n) _____ of a cardboard cereal box.

12. If only he could match his _____ on the basketball court with a high level of excellence in the classroom!

13. During the long summer afternoons, we used to sit on the shaded veranda _____ iced drinks and talking about life.

14. The reference material you have given me is interesting, but most of it is not _____ to my term paper.

15. If the contract was framed by a good lawyer, it will _____ exactly when, where, and how payment is to be made.

16. His refusal to discuss even the possibility of a compromise convinced me that I was faced with a(n) _____ opponent.

17. We could hear the quarterback's _____ signals even above the roar of the crowd.

18. The "monster" that frightened you so much during the hike last week was just a(n) _____ water snake.

19. How quickly their _____ holiday mood became quiet and sober when they had to return to work on Monday morning!

20. I enjoy Don's jokes, but he ought to bear in mind that there are certain standards of _____ to be observed at graduation.

Synonyms *From the words for this unit, choose the one that is most nearly **the same** in meaning as each of the following groups of expressions. Write the word on the line provided at the right.*

1. a replica, duplicate, reproduction, clone _____

2. feeble, impotent; unobjectionable; insipid _____

3. final terms _____

4. seemliness, good form, propriety _____

5. relentless, inexorable, unappeasable _____

6. an exclusive license; evident, plain _____

7. hostility, enmity, aversion, bad blood _____

8. compulsion, intimidation, coercion _____

9. a property, possession, holding, endowment _____

10. thundering, booming, deafening, ear-splitting _____

11. unruffled, composed, cool and collected _____

12. lively, ebullient, irrepressible; lavish _____

13. valor, courage, heroism; mastery, proficiency _____

14. to specify, require, contract, provide for _____

15. to counter, oppose, work against _____

16. tiny, minuscule, microscopic; unnoticeable _____

17. to swallow, gulp, quaff; to assimilate, digest _____

18. concern, pity, commiseration, empathy _____

19. appropriate, relevant, fit, apt, apposite _____

20. to assail, harass, badger, pester, torment _____

Antonyms From the words for this unit, choose the one that is most nearly **opposite** in meaning to each of the following groups of expressions. Write the word on the line provided at the right.

1. inappropriate, unsuitable, irrelevant _____

2. depressed, despondent, sulky _____

3. hushed, inaudible, whispered, mute _____

4. to eject, emit, expel, discharge _____

5. harmful, dangerous, pernicious, toxic, virulent _____

6. indifference, callousness, heartlessness _____

7. vast, immense, huge, infinite _____

8. a drawback, handicap, liability _____

9. lenient, indulgent, permissive; flexible _____

10. cowardice; incompetence, ineptitude _____

11. impropriety, bad form, bad taste _____

12. concealed, hidden, secret, clandestine _____

13. attraction, appeal, allure, sympathy _____

14. loud, brash; flashy, flamboyant; flighty, giddy _____

15. persuasion, coaxing, "sweet-talk," cajolery _____

16. a variation, modification, permutation _____

Choosing the Right Word
*Encircle the **boldface** word that more satisfactorily completes each of the following sentences.*

1. We soon learned that behind the woman's modest and (**stentorian, sedate**) appearance, there were an iron determination and a sharp temper.

2. As he watched his house go up in flames, he felt that he was the victim of an (**innocuous, implacable**) fate.

3. Many of the lessons that we learned during the Great Depression are (**implacable, applicable**) to our economic problems today.

4. The politician's poor showing in the polls and the failure of his fund-raising efforts (**militated, stipulated**) against his entering the Senate race.

5. "Here's the (**ultimatum, antipathy**)," said Father: "Pass all your courses, or forget about attending the Senior Prom."

6. The mistake in identification was so (**patent, infinitesimal**) that the suspect was released with the apologies of the arresting officer.

7. Mistaking the (**sedate, stentorian**) backfire of the truck for a sudden burst of gunfire, we ducked behind a parked car for safety.

8. Although he was (**beset, stipulated**) by creditors, a tough employer, and medical problems, he never seemed to lose his zest for living.

9. You are in deep trouble if you combine a strong taste for high living with an equally strong (**antipathy, compassion**) for hard work.

10. They were so (**exuberant, innocuous**) in their praise that I soon began to suspect either their judgment or their sincerity.

11. What good does it do to include all those (**stipulations, facsimiles**) in the agreement if there are no provisions for enforcing them?

12. My study of astronomy gave me a sense of the (**infinitesimal, exuberant**) importance of man and his tiny planet in a boundless universe.

13. Jim's most valuable (**prowess, asset**) may be his ability to listen quietly, even when he doesn't fully understand what is being said.

14. It does little good to feel (**decorum, compassion**) for those less fortunate than ourselves if we are not willing to make sacrifices to help them.

15. His (**prowess, duress**) as a speaker and debater quickly made him one of the leading figures in the Senate.

16. Her sense of (**compassion, decorum**) is so strict that she often makes other people feel stiff and uncomfortable.

17. In this synthetic world of ours, I sometimes wonder if my life is genuine or just a(n) (**ultimatum, facsimile**) of the real thing.

18. The authorities suspected that the hostage's statement was not made voluntarily, but under (**duress, patent**).

19. The tough leadership we need in these troubled times will not come from uncertain and (**applicable, innocuous**) personalities.

20. Without actually understanding much of what the speaker was saying, the audience seemed to (**imbibe, beset**) her optimism and vigor.

Definitions

Note carefully the spelling, pronunciation, and definition of each of the following words. Then write the word in the blank space in the illustrative phrase following.

1. alacrity
(ə 'lak rə tē)
(*n.*) a cheerful readiness; brisk and eager action
respond with _____

2. alleviate
(ə 'lē vē āt)
(*v.*) to relieve, make more bearable
_____ the patient's pain

3. antithesis
(an 'tith ə sis)
(*n.*) the direct opposite; a sharp contrast
the _____ of what I had hoped for

4. appall
(ə 'pôl)
(*v.*) to fill with dismay or horror
_____ at the thought of another war

5. bellicose
('bel i kōs)
(*adj.*) warlike in manner or temperament; quarrelsome
_____ young army officers

6. disparage
(dis 'pâr ij)
(*v.*) to belittle, speak slightingly of; to undervalue
resented his efforts to _____ us

7. dissonant
('dis ə nənt)
(*adj.*) not in harmony; disagreeing, at odds
the piercing clamor of _____ voices

8. droll
(drōl)
(*adj.*) amusingly odd
delighted by her _____ wit

9. edict
('ē dikt)
(*n.*) an order issued by someone in authority
ruled by royal _____

10. elucidate
(i 'lü sə dāt)
(*v.*) to clarify, explain
try to _____ the text

11. laud
(lôd)
(*v.*) to praise
_____ the students for their grades

12. loll
(läl)
(*v.*) to act in a lazy manner, lounge; to recline, droop
_____ in the hammock

13. loquacious
(lō 'kwā shəs)
(*adj.*) talkative, wordy; fond of talking
impatient with the _____ chairman

14. magnanimous
(mag 'nan ə məs)
(*adj.*) generous in forgiving, above small meannesses
_____ toward his former enemies

15. mandatory
('man də tôr ē)
(*adj.*) required, obligatory
receive a _____ increase in salary

16. nondescript
('nän də skript)
(*adj.*) ordinary, not outstanding; not easily classified
not pleased with the _____ clothing

17. phlegmatic
(fleg ′mat ik)

(*adj.*) slow-moving, sluggish; unemotional

impatient with his _____ disposition

18. rescind
(ri ′sind)

(*v.*) to repeal, cancel

_____ earlier laws

19. vivacious
(və ′vā shəs)

(*adj.*) lively, sprightly, full of energy

enjoy the company of _____ youths

20. whet
(whet)

(*v.*) to sharpen, make keen or eager

served to _____ my curiosity

Completing the Sentence

From the words for this unit, choose the one that best completes each of the following sentences. Write the word in the space provided.

1. The principal finally _____ the unfair school regulation that prevented new students from trying out for the varsity teams.

2. I much preferred to enjoy the paintings quietly, without listening to the "explanations" of the _____ guide.

3. Even the state troopers, who had been hardened by long experience, were _____ when they came on the scene of the automobile accident.

4. George's disposition is so _____ that he is apt to turn a simple difference of opinion into a full-scale donnybrook.

5. I shall never forget Lucy's _____ offer to coach me, even though we were competing for the same role in the play.

6. In spite of her inexperience as a programmer, she attacked her new job with _____ and made good progress.

7. At that dull, stodgy party, her _____ personality was like a breath of fresh air.

8. You can make requests and suggestions if you wish, but please don't issue any _____ .

9. Instead of waiting for government help, let's do all we can right now to _____ the sufferings of the flood victims.

10. His enthusiastic and colorful description of the new series on public TV has _____ my desire to see it.

11. Unlike Stan, I have never been in France, but is that any reason for him to _____ my efforts to speak French?

12. Although in America voting is not _____ , every qualified citizen has a duty to go to the polls in every election.

13. His idle, pleasure-seeking way of life is the exact _____ of all that his hardworking parents had expected of him.

14. Though her friends _____ her achievements, her enemies ridiculed them.

15. When the speaker tried to _____ his explanation of solar energy, I became more confused than ever.

16. I'm usually quite energetic, but there are times when I want to do nothing but _____ about and listen to my favorite albums.

17. Is this _____ little house the "magnificent mansion" that you've been telling us about all these weeks?

18. Maggie's sarcastic remarks introduced a(n) _____ note into what had been a harmonious meeting.

19. He may appear to be _____ , but his friends are aware of the strong emotions simmering beneath his quiet exterior.

20. In a time of fast-talking, slambang comedians, is there a place for his kind of quiet, _____ humor?

21. Eager to get to the beach early, we accepted Rae's offer of a ride with _____ .

22. If you hope to get a teaching license someday, you will have to meet all the _____ requirements.

23. What a difference between the nervous, highstrung thoroughbred and the _____ pack horse!

Synonyms   *From the words for this unit, choose the one that is most nearly **the same** in meaning as each of the following groups of expressions. Write the word on the line provided at the right.*

1. unselfish, charitable, noble, bighearted _____

2. grating, strident, unmelodious; irreconcilable _____

3. to hail, extol, glorify, exalt _____

4. to interpret, expound, explicate _____

5. lively, spirited, animated, ebullient _____

6. to hone, put an edge on; to excite, stimulate _____

7. gossipy, voluble, garrulous; long-winded _____

8. comical, humorous, whimsical, zany _____

9. to withdraw, revoke, retract, annul, abrogate _____

10. the opposite, contrary, antipode _____

11. lethargic, indolent, torpid; stolid, impassive _____

12. promptness, willingness, dispatch, celerity _____

13. plain, unremarkable, ordinary, unimpressive _____

14. compulsory, requisite; imperative _____

15. aggressive, combative, belligerent _____

16. to shock, stun, stupefy; horrify _____

17. a command, decree, proclamation _____

18. to degrade, decry, run down; to underrate _____

19. to lessen, lighten, allay, mitigate, assuage _____

20. to lounge, loaf, loiter; to sag, dangle _____

Antonyms   From the words for this unit, choose the one that is most nearly **opposite** in meaning to each of the following groups of expressions. Write the word on the line provided at the right.

1. to obscure, becloud, muddy up, obfuscate _____

2. petty, selfish; unforgiving, spiteful _____

3. to criticize, censure, belittle, disparage _____

4. humorless, solemn, dour _____

5. harmonious, agreeing, euphonious _____

6. emotional, sensitive, thin-skinned; excitable _____

7. distinctive, remarkable, vivid, prepossessing _____

8. optional, voluntary, discretionary _____

9. silent, reticent, closemouthed, terse, taciturn _____

10. to praise, extol, laud; to "plug" _____

11. amicable, peaceable, conciliatory, pacific _____

12. dull, spiritless, listless, indolent, languid _____

13. to dull, blunt; to deaden, stifle, dampen _____

14. to please, cheer, gladden, elate, exhilarate _____

15. reluctance, unwillingness, hesitancy _____

16. to affirm, endorse. uphold, ratify _____

110

Choosing the Right Word *Encircle the **boldface** word that more satisfactorily completes each of the following sentences.*

1. In the fight against air pollution, many states have made filtering devices (**phlegmatic, mandatory**) for all cars sold within their borders.

2. The cake was delicious, but the serving was so small that it did little more than (**elucidate, whet**) my appetite.

3. The only truly effective way to (**alleviate, appall**) the poverty of third-world nations is to help increase their capacity to produce wealth.

4. I see no reason to (**laud, elucidate**) him in such glowing terms for doing no more than his duty.

5. Her manner of speaking is so (**phlegmatic, vivacious**) that even her most commonplace remarks seem to suggest charm and excitement.

6. Observers doubted that any coalition composed of such (**magnanimous, dissonant**) factions could long refrain from petty infighting.

7. Edna pretended to be indifferent about going to the dance, but I noticed that she accepted Harry's invitation with (**loquacity, alacrity**).

8. I am waiting for you to (**elucidate, alleviate**) those ambiguous remarks about my family tree!

9. Because of the incidents that occurred during hazing week, the school may (**whet, rescind**) the rules that allow fraternity initiations.

10. In the eyes of such leaders as Gandhi and Martin Luther King, violence is the very (**edict, antithesis**) of a civilized society.

11. There is an old tradition that women are more (**loquacious, phlegmatic**) than men, but all the men I know do their full share of talking.

12. His jokes were actually not too good, but his (**nondescript, droll**) manner of delivering them made a big hit with the audience.

13. There must be a serious flaw in the character of those who make it a habit to (**alleviate, disparage**) the abilities of their best friends.

14. The houses in that development are a mixture of (**vivacious, nondescript**) styles, with no particular architectural character or taste.

15. Churchill told his countrymen to be resolute in war, defiant in defeat, and (**magnanimous, loquacious**) in victory.

16. What (**appalled, alleviated**) us even more than the fearful living conditions was the fact that the refugees seemed to have lost all hope.

17. Only an unusually (**phlegmatic, vivacious**) person could have remained calm in the face of such provocation.

18. The expression "What goes up must come down" might be termed an (**antithesis, edict**) of nature.

19. Would you rather (**droll, loll**) in the back seat of a chauffeured limousine, or drive your own convertible?

20. Although Americans are not a (**bellicose, phlegmatic**) people, they have proven themselves prepared to defend their nation at any cost.

Definitions

Note carefully the spelling, pronunciation, and definition of each of the following words. Then write the word in the blank space in the illustrative phrase following.

1. **abrasive**
   (ə 'brā siv)
   (*adj.*) causing irritation, harsh; grinding or wearing down; (*n.*) a substance used to smooth or polish

   angered by your _____ words

2. **acclimate**
   ('ak lə māt)
   (*v.*) to adapt to a new climate, environment, or situation

   _____ oneself to a new school

3. **chagrin**
   (shə 'grin)
   (*n.*) irritation or humiliation caused by disappointment or frustration; (*v.*) to cause such a feeling

   feel _____ at not being invited

4. **complacent**
   (kəm 'lā sənt)
   (*adj.*) self-satisfied; overly content

   a _____ air of superiority

5. **concur**
   (kən 'kər)
   (*v.*) to express agreement, approve

   _____ with the decision of the group

6. **defamation**
   (def ə 'mā shən)
   (*n.*) slander or libel

   sue for _____ of character

7. **explicate**
   ('eks plə kāt)
   (*v.*) to make plain or clear, explain; to interpret

   _____ a theorem in geometry

8. **fracas**
   ('frā kəs)
   (*n.*) a noisy quarrel or brawl

   involved in a violent street _____

9. **grotesque**
   (grō 'tesk)
   (*adj.*) unnatural, distorted; bizarre

   the gargoyle's _____ face

10. **pandemonium**
    (pan də 'mō nē əm)
    (*n.*) a wild uproar, din, or commotion

    fell into a state of _____

11. **raucous**
    ('rô kəs)
    (*adj.*) disagreeably harsh-sounding; disorderly

    _____ yelling at the wrestling match

12. **receptive**
    (rī 'sep tiv)
    (*adj.*) open and responsive to ideas or suggestions

    not _____ to criticism of their work

13. **renounce**
    (rī 'naůns)
    (*v.*) to give up or resign something

    _____ her share of the reward

14. **repress**
    (rī 'pres)
    (*v.*) to hold back; to put down or check by force

    _____ an impulse to cough

15. **reticent**
    ('ret ə sənt)
    (*adj.*) not inclined to speak; reserved

    _____ about expressing her opinions

16. savory
('sāv ə rē)

(*adj.*) tasty, pleasing in taste or smell; appetizing

the _____ odor of pizza

17. somnolent
('säm nə lənt)

(*adj.*) sleepy, drowsy; inducing sleep

arouse the _____ students

18. vehement
('vē ə mənt)

(*adj.*) intense, forceful, powerful

_____ objections to the plan

19. voluble
('väl yə bəl)

(*adj.*) characterized by a ready flow of words; glib, fluent

a _____ door-to-door salesperson

20. zealous
('zel əs)

(*adj.*) eager, earnest, devoted

a _____ follower of the Indian guru

Completing the Sentence

From the words for this unit, choose the one that best completes each of the following sentences. Write the word in the space provided.

1. I was confident that after Dad had eaten a good meal, he would be in a more _____ mood to my request for the use of the car.

2. When he first went out for the team, he was just an average player, but we all admired his _____ efforts to improve his game.

3. Although I am afraid of the dentist, I must _____ my fears and go for treatment.

4. _____ shouts and boos from the stands will have no effect on a good umpire's decisions.

5. The carpenter used a(n) _____ to remove the old finish from the top of the desk before revarnishing

6. The library became a scene of _____ when those "practical jokers" released a number of mice.

7. I have great respect for your knowledge of our government, but I cannot _____ with your opinion about the role of the judiciary.

8. There I was at the chalkboard unable to solve the problem while the entire class looked on. What _____ !

9. The answers the candidate gave at the press conference were rambling and _____ but contained practically no hard information.

10. Since hockey players often crash into each other at high speed, it's not surprising that occasionally a(n) _____ develops.

11. He tried hard to remain awake after dinner, but the _____ atmosphere of the musty old parlor was too much for him.

12. When we reached Mexico City, at an elevation of over 7000 feet, we found it difficult at first to _____ ourselves to the thinner air.

13. The editorial on city government was so unfair and biased that it amounted to _____ of all the elected officials of this community.

14. In an amazingly short time and with only the simplest ingredients, Bob had a(n) _____ stew simmering on the stove.

15. An accountant tried to _____ the new tax legislation to me, but when she had finished, I felt even further in the dark than before.

16. We didn't expect such _____ dislike of country-and-western music from a native of Nashville.

17. A free people cannot afford to grow _____ but must remain ever vigilant in safeguarding their liberties.

18. For Halloween the children made _____ masks that they were sure would terrorize the neighbors.

19. Both sons agreed to _____ claims to their father's estate in favor of their widowed mother.

20. The conceited actor was anything but _____ in discussing his innumerable triumphs on the stage, screen, and TV.

Synonyms   *From the words for this unit, choose the one that is most nearly **the same** in meaning as each of the following groups of expressions. Write the word on the line provided at the right.*

1. to repudiate, disown; to abdicate, abjure   _____

2. to clarify, elucidate, untangle, spell out   _____

3. boisterous, clamorous, disorderly, strident   _____

4. smug, self-satisfied, pleased with oneself   _____

5. chaos, tumult, bedlam, a three-ring circus   _____

6. groggy, nodding off; soporific   _____

7. vexation, mortification; to abash, mortify   _____

8. loquacious, garrulous; long-winded, prolix   _____

9. a row, altercation, rhubarb, brouhaha   _____

10. to subdue, curb, stifle, to constrain, bottle up   _____

11. emphatic, fierce, vigorous, impassioned   _____

12. vilification, calumny, mudslinging   _____

13. open-minded, tolerant; amenable _____

14. delectable, flavorful, aromatic, piquant _____

15. ardent, fervent, devout, dogged, "gung ho" _____

16. to grow accustomed, learn the ropes _____

17. to agree, assent; to ratify, sanction _____

18. taciturn, closemouthed, tight-lipped _____

19. fantastic, outlandish; ugly, deformed _____

20. chafing, grating, rasping, errosive _____

Antonyms   *From the words for this unit, choose the one that is most nearly* **opposite** *in meaning to each of the following groups of expressions. Write the word on the line provided at the right.*

1. to confuse, bewilder; to obscure, obfuscate _____

2. placid, tranquil, peaceful, serene, pastoral _____

3. to retain, secure; to affirm, assent, aver _____

4. discontented, chagrined _____

5. distasteful, unpalatable; malodorous _____

6. talkative, garrulous, voluble, long-winded _____

7. alert, lively, wide-awake; stimulating _____

8. a salute, tribute, testimonial; praise _____

9. narrow-minded, intolerant, hidebound _____

10. smooth, polished, satiny; oily, unctuous _____

11. to differ, disagree, part company _____

12. uncommunicative, reticent, taciturn; terse _____

13. jubilation, exultation, triumph; to exult, delight _____

14. appealing, attractive, comely _____

15. order, calm, tranquility, peace, repose _____

16. to liberate, set loose; to provoke, excite _____

17. reluctant, unwilling, averse, hanging back _____

18. agreement, accord, unanimity, harmony _____

19. apathetic, lukewarm; subdued, muted _____

Choosing the Right Word | *Encircle the **boldface** word that more satisfactorily completes each of the following sentences.*

1. We all have impulses to violence, but if we are to live in a civilized society, we must learn to (**repress, concur**) them.

2. After a month in the country, we found the sounds of rush-hour traffic in the big city more (**raucous, receptive**) than ever.

3. He has a good deal of ability, but his (**zealous, abrasive**) personality has prevented him from getting ahead in the business world.

4. (**Pandemonium, Defamation**) erupted when the nervous theater manager announced to the waiting crowd that the rock concert was cancelled.

5. It's not surprising that after so many years in the Marine Corps, he has found it difficult to become (**acclimated, repressed**) to civilian life.

6. A (**fracas, defamation**) between rival groups on the floor of the convention was swiftly quelled by security men.

7. He was, I am afraid, more (**zealous, voluble**) in promoting his own career than in seeking to help the people who had elected him.

8. Mr. Sanderson is usually a man of very few words, but he was certainly (**abrasive, voluble**) when we asked him about his operation.

9. Gloria's kind words put me in such a (**receptive, savory**) frame of mind that I agreed to work on the committee before I knew what I was doing.

10. After a lot of persuading, our parents (**repressed, concurred**) in our plans to make a bicycle tour of New England.

11. Why should he be so talkative about most things but so (**voluble, reticent**) about his own personal background?

12. For centuries scholars have argued over how to (**explicate, renounce**) certain cryptic passages in Shakespeare.

13. Lacking a positive program of his own, he hoped to gain the support of the voters by (**concurring, defaming**) the other candidates.

14. With deep (**pandemonium, chagrin**), I must confess that I was the one who neglected to hire the orchestra for the class dance.

15. Will I ever again sleep as deeply as I did on those deliciously (**somnolent, raucous**) afternoons on that hot, quiet beach!

16. In unforgettable words, the prophet Micah called on men to (**acclimate, renounce**) the use of armed force.

17. The figures in the surrealistic painting had the (**grotesque, reticent**) appearance of characters in a nightmare.

18. I was startled not so much by his disapproval of my proposal as by the (**chagrin, vehemence**) with which he denounced it.

19. While the rest of us struggled with the math problem, Meg's (**receptive, complacent**) smirk as much as announced that she had already solved it.

20. Without work to challenge his ability and give him a sense of purpose, he felt that life had lost its (**savor, somnolence**).

Analogies   *In each of the following, encircle the item that best completes the comparison.*

1. **savory** is to **taste** as
   a. abrasive is to sight
   b. raucous is to sound
   c. exuberant is to odor
   d. patent is to texture

2. **jubilant** is to **chagrin** as
   a. phlegmatic is to alacrity
   b. magnanimous is to liberality
   c. sedate is to decorum
   d. vivacious is to liveliness

3. **somnolent** is to **doze** as
   a. vivacious is to militate
   b. implacable is to rescind
   c. reticent is to divulge
   d. indolent is to loll

4. **sedate** is to **exuberant** as
   a. complacent is to mandatory
   b. nondescript is to dull
   c. applicable is to relevant
   d. reticent is to loquacious

5. **small** is to **infinitesimal** as
   a. large is to innocuous
   b. fat is to voluble
   c. big is to gigantic
   d. wide is to vehement

6. **patent** is to **invention** as
   a. trademark is to brand
   b. license is to vehicle
   c. copyright is to book
   d. title is to name

7. **complacent** is to **disgruntled** as
   a. zealous is to indifferent
   b. stentorian is to raucous
   c. mandatory is to vehement
   d. receptive is to retentive

8. **laud** is to **praise** as
   a. explicate is to appall
   b. concur is to defame
   c. repress is to cancel
   d. disparage is to belittle

9. **elucidate** is to **clearer** as
   a. stipulate is to newer
   b. alleviate is to milder
   c. acclimate is to stranger
   d. rescind is to stronger

10. **asset** is to **liability** as
   a. apple is to orange
   b. north is to east
   c. plus is to minus
   d. black is to green

11. **abdicate** is to **throne** as
   a. stipulate is to condition
   b. deliver is to ultimatum
   c. enforce is to edict
   d. renounce is to title

12. **facsimile** is to **same** as
   a. prowess is to opposite
   b. antipathy is to same
   c. antithesis is to opposite
   d. ultimatum is to same

13. **zeal** is to **fervent** as
   a. prowess is to valorous
   b. chagrin is to exuberant
   c. compassion is to reticent
   d. magnaminity is to stentorian

14. **vivacious** is to **phlegmatic** as
   a. hearty is to merry
   b. carefree is to careless
   c. vehement is to grotesque
   d. jaunty is to morose

15. **bellicose** is to **threaten** as
   a. nondescript is to whet
   b. droll is to amuse
   c. innocuous is to appall
   d. grotesque is to comfort

16. **voluble** is to **much** as
   a. loquacious is to little
   b. complacent is to much
   c. reticent is to little
   d. infinitesimal is to much

17. **silence** is to **pandemonium** as
   a. dignity is to decorum
   b. order is to anarchy
   c. quarrel is to fracas
   d. force is to duress

18. **stimulate** is to **interest** as
   a. repress is to laughter
   b. whet is to appetite
   c. beset is to pleasure
   d. imbibe is to mouth

receptive is to **take in** as
a. sedate is to wake up
b. mandatory is to wipe out
c. dissonant is to smooth out
d. abrasive is to wear down

20. **magnanimous** is to **favorable** as
a. raucous is to unfavorable
b. nondescript is to favorable
c. vivacious is to unfavorable
d. grotesque is to favorable

Spelling All of the following words, correctly spelled, were introduced in Units 13–15. Underline the word that is **incorrectly** spelled in each of the following groups. Then supply the correct spelling in the space provided.

resind	concur	mandatory	_____
patent	disonant	chagrin	_____
stipulate	elucidate	infinitesimal	_____
aleviate	explicate	whet	_____
nondescript	pandimonium	laud	_____
decorum	apall	disparage	_____
implacable	sedate	flegmatic	_____
locquacious	repress	somnolent	_____
compassion	abrasive	voluable	_____
militate	complasent	vehement	_____
beset	fracas	inocuous	_____
defamation	aclimate	grotesque	_____
durress	reticent	prowess	_____
applicabel	facsimile	stentorian	_____
antithesis	droll	bellecose	_____

Identification In each of the following groups, encircle the word that is best defined or suggested by the introductory phrase.

an official proclamation with the force of law
a. droll   b. chagrin   c. edict   d. grotesque

a salesman known for his fast, smooth talk
a. reticent   b. voluble   c. abrasive   d. phlegmatic

This is my final offer—take it or leave it!
a. asset   b. ultimatum   c. antithesis   d. savory

grounds for a lawsuit
a. prowess   b. defamation   c. ultimatum   d. edict

a child who listens carefully and learns readily
a. sedate   b. implacable   c. nondescript   d. receptive

a fight on the field soon broken up by the officials
a. alacrity   b. decorum   c. patent   d. fracas

7. the world's greatest high jumper
a. chagrin   b. prowess   c. defamation   d. antipathy

8. getting adjusted to a new job
a. sedated   b. acclimated   c. disparaged   d. whetted

9. to include as a special point in a contract
a. imbibe   b. stipulate   c. laud   d. renounce

10. I was never so embarrassed in my life.
a. chagrined   b. reticent   c. raucous   d. zealous

11. "I do not like you, Dr. Fell. The reason why I cannot tell."
a. antipathy   b. ultimatum   c. antithesis   d. edict

12. a medicine with a formula that may not be copied
a. applicable   b. sedate   c. mandatory   d. patent

13. accept an offer with cheerful promptness
a. alacrity   b. decorum   c. duress   d. defamation

14. Please explain what you meant by those remarks!
a. alleviate   b. rescind   c. elucidate   d. acclimate

15. spent the entire afternoon in the hammock
a. rescind   b. loll   c. beset   d. stipulate

16. sympathy for those less fortunate than ourselves
a. compassion   b. facsimile   c. decorum   d. antithesis

17. the exact opposite of what was expected
a. alacrity   b. antithesis   c. decorum   d. facsimile

18. children at a party running about in wild disorder
a. chagrin   b. savory   c. edict   d. pandemonium

19. overcome with shock and dismay
a. appalled   b. whetted   c. stipulated   d. beset

20. like the cat that swallowed the canary
a. complacent   b. droll   c. savory   d. grotesque

Antonyms   *In each of the following groups, encircle the word or expression that is most nearly the **opposite** of the first word in **boldface type**.*

1. mandatory
a. optional
b. greedy
c. silent
d. needed

2. imbibe
a. eject
b. hurt
c. help
d. praise

3. laud
a. appall
b. elucidate
c. disparage
d. beset

4. innocuous
a. kind
b. harmful
c. necessary
d. open

5. savory
a. ugly
b. distasteful
c. settled
d. costly

6. facsimile
a. speed
b. difficulty
c. original
d. cruelty

7. asset
a. dislike
b. disagreement
c. ability
d. disadvantage

8. abrasive
a. discouraging
b. hard
c. forceful
d. soothing

9. implacable	**12. concur**	**15. phlegmatic**	**18. stipulate**
a. severe	a. join	a. strong	a. demand
b. flexible	b. bring	b. strange	b. take
c. laughable	c. disagree	c. lively	c. agree
d. poor	d. please	d. amusing	d. renounce
10. stentorian	**13. raucous**	**16. defamation**	**19. reticent**
a. repeated	a. small	a. praise	a. grotesque
b. tiny	b. mellow	b. advantage	b. receptive
c. seated	c. dangerous	c. pity	c. voluble
d. hushed	d. safe	d. agreement	d. applicable
11. magnanimous	**14. nondescript**	**17. droll**	**20. vehement**
a. sleepy	a. funny	a. loud	a. strong
b. mean	b. lively	b. large	b. weak
c. slow	c. distinctive	c. funny	c. messy
d. eager	d. confusing	d. grim	d. convincing

Completing the Sentence *From the following list of words, choose the one that best completes each of the sentences below. Write the word in the appropriate space.*

Group A

imbibe	whet	antipathy	prowess
applicable	decorum	chagrin	pandemonium
repress	receptive	alacrity	rescind

1. The long wait in line to get into the stadium only _____ our appetite to see the big game.
2. We cannot _____ helpful traffic regulations simply because some drivers don't like them.
3. I think that we should make an effort to behave with more _____ during the assembly period.
4. The statistics you have cited may be accurate, but in my opinion they are not _____ to the problem facing us now.
5. Her _____ as a figure skater has made her both rich and famous.

Group B

implacable	asset	appall	savory
antithesis	facsimile	stentorian	elucidate
somnolent	ultimatum	mandatory	edict

1. The candidate's ability to speak effectively to all kinds of audiences proved an invaluable _____ during the long campaign.
2. The two brothers look much alike, but in personality and character each is the _____ of the other.

3. The night was punctuated by the _____ boom of the heav‹
artillery.

4. My Uncle Morris didn't just offer advice or make requests; he delivered
a(n) _____ that he expected to be obeyed.

5. We were trying hard to be alert, but the heavy food, the warm room, and
the drone of his voice quickly put us into a(n) _____ state‹

Word Families

A. *On the line provided, write a* **noun form** *of each of the following words.*

EXAMPLE: zealous — **zeal**

1. stipulate _____

2. exuberant _____

3. renounce _____

4. disparage _____

5. magnanimous _____

6. receptive _____

7. alleviate _____

8. abrasive _____

9. grotesque _____

10. reticent _____

11. elucidate _____

12. acclimate _____

13. concur _____

14. explicate _____

15. repress _____

16. sedate _____

17. bellicose _____

18. dissonant _____

19. loquacious _____

B. *On the line provided, write a* **verb** *related to each of the following words.*

EXAMPLE: defamation — **defame**

1. savory _____

2. applicable _____

3. receptive _____

4. abrasive _____

5. mandatory _____

**Filling
the Blanks**   *Encircle the pair of words that best complete the
meaning of each of the following passages.*

1. I might not be so _____ about suggesting improvements at
   the office if my boss were more _____ to constructive
   criticism. But since he seems to resent it, I keep such ideas to myself.
   a. phlegmatic . . . implacable   c. reticent . . . receptive
   b. zealous . . . magnanimous   d. exuberant . . . compassionate

2. Though the supply of winter uniforms had done much to _____
   the hardship suffered by the troops, the continuing shortage of ammunition
   and the ominous weather forecast _____ against pressing
   the attack.
   a. beset . . . concurred   c. acclimate . . . stipulated
   b. alleviate . . . militated   d. whet . . . elucidated

3. Though it didn't rule out mild soap, the warranty expressly _____
   that _____ cleansers should not be used on the floor, since
   they would damage the tile surface.
   a. stipulated . . . abrasive   c. rescinded . . . applicable
   b. explicated . . . innocuous   d. concurred . . . dissonant

4. Alexander the Great was a(n) _____ foe of the Persians as
   long as they posed a threat to Greek security. But once he had conquered
   them, he proved to be a(n) _____ and even-handed ruler.
   a. vehement . . . repressive   c. phlegmatic . . . nondescript
   b. somnolent . . . innocuous   d. implacable . . . magnanimous

5. "Since the documents are only _____ of the Declaration of
   Independence," the salesperson said, "the price I'm asking for them is
   _____ in comparison to what the real thing would cost."
   a. antitheses . . . grotesque   c. patents . . . colossal
   b. facsimiles . . . infinitesimal   d. edicts . . . voluble

6. Like a Roman emperor of old, the new principal issued a(n) _____
   stating that attendance at morning assembly, which had been optional
   under the old regime, was now _____ .
   a. edict . . . mandatory   c. patent . . . complacent
   b. facsimile . . . applicable   d. defamation . . . sedate

7. Edna's _____ , offbeat sense of humor proved to be a
   considerable _____ in the competition for class wit.
   a. nondescript . . . facsimile   c. savory . . . fracas
   b. grotesque . . . antithesis   d. droll . . . asset

Analogies *In each of the following, encircle the item that best completes the comparison.*

1. laggard is to **alacrity** as
a. renegade is to duplicity
b. martinet is to discipline
c. bully is to belligerence
d. craven is to valor

2. zealous is to **apathy** as
a. ardent is to enthusiasm
b. sophomoric is to maturity
c. brash is to temerity
d. omniscient is to knowledge

3. antipathy is to **abhor** as
a. loathing is to laud
b. fondness is to relish
c. dislike is to esteem
d. partiality is to appall

4. claim is to **renounce** as
a. sword is to brandish
b. indemnity is to recompense
c. wrong is to redress
d. right is to waive

5. innocuous is to **virulent** as
a. placid is to turbulent
b. receptive is to amenable
c. disheveled is to unkempt
d. dour is to obnoxious

6. garrulous is to **loquacious** as
a. sedate is to vivacious
b. parsimonious is to magnanimous
c. scrupulous is to meticulous
d. nocturnal is to culinary

7. implacable is to **clemency** as
a. clairvoyant is to sensitivity
b. ingenuous is to guile
c. chivalrous is to magnanimity
d. stolid is to integrity

8. patent is to **clandestine** as
a. explicit is to tacit
b. urbane is to suave
c. decrepit is to obsolete
d. endemic is to negligible

9. abrasive is to **erode** as
a. conclusive is to flood
b. coercive is to plunder
c. tentative is to demolish
d. corrosive is to burn

10. pungent is to **smell** as
a. musty is to touch
b. gnarled is to hearing
c. savory is to taste
d. fallow is to sight

11. crestfallen is to **chagrin** as
a. elated is to exhilaration
b. complacent is to apprehension
c. blithe is to dismay
d. somber is to compunction

12. speech is to **voluble** as
a. food is to palatable
b. income is to multifarious
c. writing is to voluminous
d. thought is to spontaneous

13. contentious is to **bellicose** as
a. mandatory is to optional
b. recalcitrant is to receptive
c. squalid is to opulent
d. truculent is to belligerent

14. chaos is to **turbulent** as
a. conflagration is to dissonant
b. pandemonium is to raucous
c. holocaust is to sonorous
d. fracas is to quiescent

15. vehement is to **energy** as
a. potent is to edge
b. cogent is to force
c. trenchant is to clout
d. acrid is to insight

16. gibes are to **disparage** as
a. platitudes are to deride
b. jeers are to commend
c. condolences are to defame
d. compliments are to extol

17. malevolent is to **rancor** as
a. phlegmatic is to torpor
b. stolid is to animosity
c. nonchalant is to concern
d. impervious is to receptivity

18. applicable is to **irrelevant** as
a. capricious is to inconstant
b. doting is to indulgent
c. kindred is to incompatible
d. copious is to inanimate

19. poignant is to **touch** as
a. limpid is to stroke
b. droll is to tickle
c. ironic is to brush
d. ominous is to rub

20. order is to **rescind** as
a. belief is to abjure
b. reference is to allude
c. agreement is to concur
d. problem is to explicate

21. grave is to **interment** as
a. shelf is to scrutiny
b. buffet is to consecrate
c. bed is to repose
d. chair is to sojourn

22. perceptible is to **discern** as
a. pliable is to stiffen
b. virulent is to control
c. indelible is to expunge
d. feasible is to do

Antonyms   *In each of the following groups, encircle the word or expression that is most nearly the **opposite** of the word in **boldface type**.*

1. exuberant
a. feasible
b. premeditated
c. oily
d. despondent

2. expunge
a. impress
b. acclimate
c. placate
d. erase

3. impetus
a. ultimatum
b. intrusion
c. curb
d. facsimile

4. discern
a. beset
b. covet
c. unearth
d. overlook

5. appall
a. imbibe
b. delight
c. fathom
d. reject

6. profess
a. stipulate
b. remove
c. disclaim
d. acquiesce

7. sedate
a. askew
b. flamboyant
c. reprehensible
d. gallant

8. invulnerable
a. consecrated
b. prolonged
c. implicated
d. exposed

9. coerce
a. militate
b. persuade
c. extirpate
d. bludgeon

10. brash
a. circumspect
b. venal
c. audacious
d. rampant

11. alleviate
a. elucidate
b. exult
c. exacerbate
d. endow

12. nocturnal
a. weekly
b. annual
c. minute
d. daytime

13. whet
a. delete
b. chisel
c. blunt
d. augment

14. infallible
a. immaculate
b. immune
c. imperfect
d. impartial

15. scrutinize
a. skim
b. plod
c. converge
d. relax

16. decrepit
a. tentative
b. vigorous
c. reticent
d. antiquated

17. repress
a. misconstrue
b. acclaim
c. muse
d. liberate

18. superficial
a. profound
b. facile
c. supple
d. frivolous

19. complacent
a. discontent
b. pliable
c. unfeigned
d. smug

20. officious
a. omnipotent
b. aloof
c. corpulent
d. stately

21. ambidextrous
a. stingy
b. punitive
c. cursory
d. maladroit

22. parsimonious
a. mercenary
b. sinuous
c. generous
d. disreputable

23. infinitesimal
a. colossal
b. finite
c. indomitable
d. negligible

24. vanguard
a. muggers
b. stragglers
c. vendors
d. backers

124

Filling the Blanks

Encircle the pair of words that best complete the meaning of each of the following passages.

1. Although I'd been wide-awake when I'd entered the auditorium, the _____ effect of the speaker's droning voice and tired platitudes was so _____ that I began to fall asleep.
   a. uncanny . . . infinitesimal
   b. lamentable . . . negligible
   c. somnolent . . . stultifying
   d. averse . . . exhilarating

2. The leering faces of _____ gargoyles and other bizarre monsters _____ from the walls, towers, and battlements of medieval churches and castles like so many fantastic hunting trophies hung over a fireplace.
   a. blithe . . . ruminate
   b. grotesque . . . protrude
   c. garrulous . . . gape
   d. supercilious . . . skulk

3. The _____ little "difference of opinion" suddenly developed into an ugly _____ when the two people involved in the dispute started throwing punches at each other.
   a. nondescript . . . antithesis
   b. squalid . . . scrutiny
   c. insidious . . . quandary
   d. amicable . . . fracas

4. When the Montagues and their _____ , the Capulets, decided to settle their feud in the streets of Verona, the authorities had to be called in to _____ the riot that ensued.
   a. adversaries . . . quell
   b. martinets . . . chastise
   c. renegades . . . repress
   d. exponents . . . suppress

5. When the weather's fine, I enjoy _____ on the beach, but when it's _____ , I prefer to bask under a sunlamp.
   a. sojourning . . . infallible
   b. reposing . . . palatable
   c. embarking . . . capricious
   d. lolling . . . inclement

6. Though _____ invariably squander their _____ in no time at all, frugal people may often amass comfortable "nest eggs" over the years.
   a. deviates . . . precedents
   b. benefactors . . . attainments
   c. wastrels . . . assets
   d. clairvoyants . . . itineraries

7. The account he gave of his actions on that fateful night was so full of _____ and inconsistencies that I did not think it would be _____ for him to convince a jury of his innocence.
   a. discrepancies . . . feasible
   b. panaceas . . . facile
   c. precedents . . . cogent
   d. gibes . . . scrupulous

8. Recognizing that an enemy assault on the right would put his entire battle formation in _____ , the commander ordered his reserve troops _____ to reinforce the exposed flank.

 a. demise . . . augmented   c. holocaust . . . coerced
 b. jeopardy . . . deployed   c. duplicity . . . retrogressed

9. The author was gratified by the lavish praise offered by the many critics who _____ her new novel, but she was perplexed and disappointed by the _____ welcome the book received from the public.

 a. extolled . . . tepid   c. reiterated . . . insidious
 b. scrutinized . . . benevolent   d. deleted . . . dour

10 The suspect had been observed _____ furtively in an alleyway an hour before the assault occurred, which suggests that a _____ crime rather than a chance mishap was involved.

 a. skulking . . . premeditated   c. plodding . . . truculent
 b. reposing . . . finite   d. brandishing . . . malevolent

11. The military governor began to grow _____ when the brutal _____ he ordered against the populace for acts of sabotage failed to curb their spirit of resistance.

 a. recalcitrant . . . condolences   c. corrosive . . . quandaries
 b. apprehensive . . . reprisals   d. assiduous . . . indemnities

12. In Pennsylvania's Amish country a visitor can still see _____ a way of life that elsewhere in this vast country has long since become _____ .

 a. copious . . . decrepit   c. extant . . . obsolete
 b. multifarious . . . emaciated   d. limpid . . . poignant

13. Copernicus, Galileo, and other _____ of the sun-centered theory of the our galaxy were in the _____ of the "scientific revolution" that has ultimately led to human beings walking on the moon.

 a. misnomers . . . plagiarism   c. wastrels . . . conflagration
 b. clairvoyants . . . retribution   d. exponents . . . vanguard

14. After our upset defeat we realized, to our _____ , that our early string of easy victories had turned us _____ and dulled our competitive edge.

 a. prowess . . . implacable   c. chagrin . . . complacent
 b. duress . . . receptive   d. alacrity . . stentorian

Final Mastery Test

I. Selecting Word Meanings

In each of the following groups, encircle the word or expression that is most nearly **the same** *in meaning as the word in* **boldface type** *in the introductory phrase.*

1. test of **fortitude**
a. skill   b. courage   c. conscience   d. intelligence

2. **augment** his income
a. insure   b. increase   c. spend   d. waste

3. an **opulent** lifestyle
a. luxurious   b. dull   c. boring   d. poverty-stricken

4. **reiterate** an opinion
a. express   b. attack   c. defend   d. repeat

5. **averse** to strenuous exercise
a. opposed   b. accustomed   c. devoted   d. untrained

6. a **bellicose** personality
a. complacent   b. boring   c. quarrelsome   d. kindly

7. place in **jeopardy**
a. jail   b. custody   c. danger   d. safety

8. become a **culinary** expert
a. world   b. cooking   c. music   d. travel

9. time to **muse**
a. entertain   b. ponder   c. relax   d. study

10. **harass** the driver
a. help   b. accompany   c. annoy   d. dismiss

11. a **malevolent** attitude
a. spiteful   b. protective   c. indifferent   d. loving

12. an **invulnerable** position
a. safe   b. dangerous   c. isolated   d. important

13. **unfeigned** interest
a. businesslike   b. private   c. sincere   d. hypocritical

14. an **omniscient** deity
a. hardworking   b. veteran   c. all-knowing   d. conscientious

15. **remiss** in her work
a. excellent   b. skilled   c. scrupulous   d. careless

16. an **infallible** method
a. foolproof   b. scientific   c. fallacious   d. unproved

17. a **diffident** visitor
a. unexpected   b. shy   c. rude   d. welcome

18. an **inopportune** time
a. early   b. late   c. inconvenient   d. pleasant

19. guilty of **duplicity**
a. murder   b. bad taste   c. stubbornness   d. deceitfulness

20. his **ominous** appearance
a. threatening   b. impressive   c. attractive   d. unexplained

21. vociferous protests
 a. frequent   b. subtle   c. noisy   d. reasonable

22. a commodious harbor
 a. distant   b. well-run   c. costly   d. roomy

23. voluminous correspondence
 a. confidential   b. abundant   c. infrequent   d. official

24. squalid conditions
 a. healthful   b. exacting   c. ideal   d. wretched

25. apprehensive feelings
 a. worried   b. elated   c. indescribable   d. unreasonable

II. Antonyms   *In each of the following groups, encircle the **two** words or expressions that are most nearly **opposite** in meaning.*

26. a. commend   b. consecrate   c. criticize   d. sacrifice
27. a. enthusiastic   b. agreeable   c. contentious   d. attentive
28. a. weak   b. potent   c. illegal   d. beneficial
29. a. confirm   b. attain   c. arouse   d. rescind
30. a. youthful   b. expected   c. dour   d. amicable
31. a. scrupulous   b. glorious   c. natural   d. cursory
32. a. incite   b. organize   c. train   d. quell
33. a. intellectual   b. petty   c. magnanimous   d. disturbed
34. a. palatable   b. dangerous   c. disagreeable   d. foolish
35. a. wealthy   b. scientific   c. assiduous   d. lazy
36. a. obey   b. antagonize   c. placate   d. remain
37. a. infinitesimal   b. loquacious   c. colossal   d. profitable
38. a. deny   b. embezzle   c. clarify   d. profess
39. a. foreign   b. disheveled   c. well-groomed   d. charming
40. a. asset   b. unwillingness   c. allure   d. alacrity

III. Supplying Words in Context   *In each of the sentences below, write in the blank space the most appropriate word chosen from the following list.*

Group A

abhor	vehement	esteem	suave
solace	consecrate	conclusive	trenchant
gibe	sedate	vivacious	suppress
temerity	guile	warily	somber

41. I find some _____ for our failure in the knowledge that we did everything we possibly could.

42. Her _____ remarks cut right to the heart of the issue under discussion.

43. The fingerprints were regarded as _____ evidence of his guilt.

44. Her _____ personality did much to enliven the party.

45. How does he have the _____ to criticize people who have done so much for him?

46. The dismal winter landscape put him in a very _____ mood.

47. Let's ignore their vicious _____ and do what we think is right.

48. He is so _____ that he seems to fit into any social situation without the slightest difficulty.

49. The dictator was unable to _____ the spirit of freedom.

50. We _____ racism, but we feel pity rather than hate for the racists.

Group B

adversary	ironic	implicate	altruistic
insidious	inveterate	condolence	dearth
multifarious	tacit	impervious	clairvoyant
misnomer	facsimile	feasible	redress

51. Isn't it _____ that he resigned from the editorship just before the newspaper received the award he had done so much to earn?

52. With all her _____ activities, it's a wonder that she finds time to sleep.

53. He is so sure of his own virtues that he is just about _____ to criticism.

54. As a(n) _____ concert-goer, he has seen many great musicians perform.

55. Janie's uncanny ability to guess what I'm thinking at any moment sometimes verges on the _____ .

56. Not a word was said, but there was a(n) _____ understanding that we would go to the dance together.

57. I'll have to be at my best to have a chance against a(n) _____ like Ken.

58. It would certainly be a(n) _____ to nickname that unscrupulous crook "Honest John."

59. The plan was deemed not _____ since there weren't sufficient funds to put it into effect.

60. Just when strong leadership is all-important, we find ourselves suffering from a(n) _____ of qualified leaders.

IV. Words Connected with Law and Government

*The words in Column A may be applied to various situations connected with law and government. In the space before each word, write the **letter** of the item in Column B that identifies it.*

Column A		Column B
_____	**61.** abjure	a. a formal command by a governmental authority
_____	**62.** punitive	b. to change or add to a law
_____	**63.** ultimatum	c. based on the will of the people
_____	**64.** defamation	d. possessing unlimited power, as a dictator
_____	**65.** edict	e. to repudiate under oath
_____	**66.** precedent	f. relating to punishment
_____	**67.** amend	g. to pass on to one's heirs
_____	**68.** mandatory	h. unfair injury to a person's good name
_____	**69.** omnipotent	i. relating to law-making
_____	**70.** bequeath	j. a final demand by a government
		k. obligatory; required by law or regulation
		l. a judicial decision serving as a basis for later decisions

V. Words That Describe People

Some words that describe people are listed below. Write the appropriate word on the line next to each of the following descriptions.

adroit	raucous	chivalrous	implacable
reprehensible	corrosive	august	indulgent
exuberant	meticulous	exemplary	sophomoric
nonchalant	stentorian	brash	officious

71. I admire the grace and courtesy with which Tom treated that elderly lady.

_____

72. She takes everything in stride and remains calm and unruffled in situations that would upset other people.

_____

73. When he feels that he has been wronged, he will never be satisfied until he "gets even."

_____

74. Ms. Heyland, our English teacher, encourages us to pay careful attention to every detail of grammar, usage, and punctuation.

_____

75. He is an outstanding citizen of this community who can well serve as a model for young people.

_____

76. She's always meddling in other people's affairs.

_____

77. I admire the cleverness and skill with which Amy handles people in situations in which others might be extremely awkward.

_____

78. Bob's foolish chatter and know-it-all attitude make him a total bore.

_____

79. He has betrayed his trust and should be condemned by all decent people.

_____

80. My aunt is so fond of her children that she lets them do almost anything they want.

_____

VI. Word Associations *In each of the following, encircle the word or expression that best completes the meaning of the sentence or answers the question, with particular reference to the meaning of the word in **boldface type.***

81. You would **extol** something that you find
a. contentious
b. commendable
c. corrosive
d. crestfallen

82. To **skulk** out of a room suggests
a. haste
b. happiness
c. sneakiness
d. listlessness

83. Which of the following suggests that a team is being **derided?**
a. "We're number one!"
b. "Go and get 'em!"
c. "You guys are losers!"
d. "Give us a break, umpire!"

84. If you **concur** in a decision, you
a. agree with it
b. consider it wrong
c. are indifferent to it
d. are not aware of it

85. To be **somnolent** implies a desire to
a. eat
b. exercise
c. get out of town
d. sleep

86. We may apply the word **stately** to
a. a duchess and a sailing ship
b. a robot and a computer
c. a city and a state
d. nostalgia and panacea

87. The word **demise** suggests that someone or something has
a. won a prize
b. failed an examination
c. passed out of existence
d. gained final approval

88. A movie that is exceptionally **poignant** is likely to
a. put you to sleep
b. touch your emotions
c. get a lot of laughs
d. fail at the box office

89. The word **holocaust** can be applied to
a. a trivial event
b. an amusing misunderstanding
c. a long war that ends in a draw
d. a historical tragedy costing many lives

90. A picture that is **askew** should be
a. dusted
b. given a price
c. straightened
d. sold to the highest bidder

91. You would criticize a **wastrel** for
a. being lazy
b. talking too loudly
c. squandering money
d. not telling the truth

92. Which nickname would a **parsimonious** person be most likely to have?
a. Alibi Ike
b. El Cheapo
c. Fancy Dan
d. Calamity Jane

93. Which of the following phrases suggests something that is **nondescript?**
a. something the cat dragged in
b. bright-eyed and bushy-tailed
c. cute as a button
d. ready for action

94. Which of the following might be called **innocuous?**
a. a neighborhood gossip
b. a devoted community worker
c. a religious leader
d. a well-meaning but ineffectual person

95. An expenditure of money is **negligible** when it is
a. illegal
b. too small to worry about
c. excessive
d. legal but not morally justified

96. A well-known **renegade** in American history is
a. Daniel Boone
b. Abigail Adams
c. Edgar Allan Poe
d. Benedict Arnold

97. If people refer to Dave as **unkempt,** he should try to
a. speak more clearly
b. improve his grooming
c. smile more often
d. learn to play bridge

98. You would be most likely to read of **uncanny** events in
a. a history textbook
b. a detective story
c. a novel of social protest
d. a ghost story

99. A nation that is a **belligerent** is engaged in
a. war
b. industrialization
c. land reform
d. energy conservation

100. Which of the following might be described as **lamentable?**
a. winning a scholarship
b. visiting a sick friend
c. getting a new car
d. failing to do well on this Final Test

Units 1-3

mis, miss, mit, mitt—to send

This root appears in **demise** (page 20). The literal meaning is "a sending down," but the word now suggests a death, especially of a person in an elevated position. Some other words based on the same root are listed below.

commissary	**emit**	**manumit**	**premise**
emissary	**intermittently**	**missile**	**remission**

From the list of words above, choose the one that corresponds to each of the brief definitions below. Write the word on the line at the right of the definition, and then in the illustrative phrase below the definition.

1. to free from slavery or bondage
    _____ the indentured servants

2. a messenger, agent (*"one sent out"*)
    _____ chosen to negotiate a surrender

3. a place where supplies are distributed; a lunchroom
    buy provisions at the _____

4. coming and going at intervals; not continuously (*"sent between"*)
    rained _____ during the night

5. an object to be thrown or shot
    fire a(n) _____ with deadly accuracy

6. a letup, abatement; a relief from suffering
    a brief _____ of the tempest

7. to release or send forth (*"send out"*)
    _____ a high-pitched warning signal

8. a statement or idea upon which a conclusion is based (*"that which is sent before"*)
    an argument based on a false _____

From the list of words above, choose the one that best completes each of the following sentences. Write the word in the space provided.

1. When he issued the Emancipation Proclamation in 1863, President Abraham Lincoln _____ four million enslaved human beings.

2. The families of the soldiers stationed on the base were able to buy food and clothing at the _____ .

3. The trapped rabbit _____ a frantic squeal and struggled in vain to escape the hawk's talons.

4. The Secretary of State went to the arms conference being held in a foreign capital as the official _____ of the United States.

5. It snowed _____ at first, stopping and starting a number of times before the steady downfall commenced.

6. The doctors had begun to give up hope when the disease suddenly went into _____ , and the patient began to recover.

7. In the hands of the old-time vaudeville comedian, a custard pie became a(n) _____ that could stop any pursuer in his or her tracks.

8. Basing his decision on the _____ that some child in the school was carrying an infectious disease, the doctor ordered all of the students to be inoculated.

Units 4-6

fac, fact—to make or do

This root appears in **facile,** "easily accomplished or done" (page 36). Some other words based on the same root are listed below.

artifact	**faction**	**factor**	**faculty**
facility	**factitious**	**factual**	**malefactor**

From the list of words above, choose the one that corresponds to each of the brief definitions below. Write the word on the line at the right of the definition, and then in the illustrative phrase below the definition.

1. based on fact, real _____

   a(n) _____ report outlining just what had happened

2. ease, skill; that which serves or acts as a convenience or for a specific function _____

   played the piano with great _____

3. a small group of people within a larger group _____

   the _____ in favor of public ownership

4. one who commits a crime, evildoer (*"one who does evil"*) _____

   arrested as a(n) _____

5. artificial, not natural; sham _____

   _____ enthusiasm for the dictator

6. one of the elements that help to bring about a result; an agent _____

   a major _____ in their success

7. an object of historical or archeological interest produced by human workmanship (*"something made with skill"*) _____

uncovered some Indian _____

8. a teaching staff; the ability to act or to do something _____

a(n) _____ for understanding people

From the list of words on page 133, choose the one that best completes each of the following sentences. Write the word in the space provided.

1. His major weakness, which keeps him from a position of leadership, is a complete lack of the _____ of self-criticism.

2. The speaker pointed out a number of ways in which we could raise the money necessary to increase the library _____ in our community.

3. The _____ of ancient cultures tell us a great deal about the day-to-day life of earlier civilizations.

4. What seems to be strong popular support for that program is in reality shallow and _____ .

5. What was once a united political party has been splintered into two or three warring _____ .

6. President Theodore Roosevelt criticized certain rich men as evildoers, calling them "_____ of great wealth."

7. Television has become a key _____ in determining public opinion and sharing popular tastes.

8. We are not dealing with opinions or interpretations but with a simple matter of _____ accuracy.

Units 7-9

voc, vok—to call

This root appears in **vociferous,** "loud or noisy" (page 55). Some other words based on the same root are listed below.

advocate	**convocation**	**evoke**	**revoke**
avocation	**equivocal**	**invoke**	**vocalize**

From the list of words above, choose the one that corresponds to each of the brief definitions below. Write the word on the line at the right of the definition, and then in the illustrative phrase below the definition.

1. to bring or call back; to annul by recalling _____

_____ a license to drive

2. to give voice to; to sing without words   _____

_____ one's fears

3. to plead in favor of; one who defends a course; one who pleads the cause of another   _____

_____ a revision of the proposal

4. open to two or more interpretations, ambiguous; uncertain or doubtful in nature   _____

a(n) _____ statement

5. a meeting, especially of members of a college or clergy ("a calling together")   _____

attend the _____

6. an occupation or activity pursued for enjoyment, in addition to one's regular work; a hobby   _____

a diverting _____

7. to call in for help or support; to appeal to as an authority; to put into effect; to make an earnest request for ("to call on")   _____

_____ their forgiveness

8. to call forth; bring to mind ("to call out")   _____

_____ a positive response

From the list of words on page 134, choose the one that best completes each of the following sentences. Write the word in the spaces provided.

1. A chemist by profession, Sarah has for many years pursued landscape painting as

a(n) _____ .

2. To warm up their voices, opera singers will _____ for a short time before going on the stage.

3. As if by magic, the actors on the bare stage _____ the sounds, shapes, and colors of a small New England town.

4. The new ordinance restricting bicycle traffic during rush hours proved to be so

unpopular that it was _____ .

5. To prevent the complete disruption of the city's transportation system, the governor

threatened to _____ the law that would send the union's leaders to jail for contempt.

6. The officer's _____ remarks suggested that he was of two minds about the enemy's will to resist.

7. The mayor has always _____ strict governmental regulation of building codes.

8. Dr. Elizabeth Mann is one of the specialists who have been invited to attend the

_____ of experts on problems in the health field.

Units 10-12

tac, tag, tang, teg, tet, ting—to touch

This root appears in **tangible**, "able to be seen or felt" (page 88). Some other words based on the same root are listed below.

contagious	**intangible**	**tact**	**tangent**
intact	**integral**	**tactile**	**tangential**

From the list of words above, choose the one that corresponds to each of the brief definitions below. Write the word on the line at the right of the definition, and then in the illustrative phrase below the definition.

1. unimpaired; whole, with no part missing   _____

    keep a collection _____

2. a keen sense of the right thing to say or do to avoid giving offense; diplomacy   _____

    show _____ in handling a delicate situation

3. essential for completeness; lacking nothing essential   _____

    a(n) _____ part of our organization

4. barely touching; only superficially relevant, digressive   _____

    a(n) _____ remark

5. capable of spreading from person to person, catching   _____

    a(n) _____ disease

6. of or relating to the sense of touch; perceptible to touch   _____

    a(n) _____ organ

7. not capable of being touched; not easily grasped by the mind   _____

    a(n) _____ asset

8. an abrupt change in course; touching at only one point   _____

    a straight line _____ to a curve

From the list of words above, choose the one that best completes each of the following sentences. Write the word in the space provided.

1. His remarks were so _____ to the subject of the discussion as to be practically beside the point.

2. If we want their support in the upcoming election, we must make their suggestions a(n) _____ part of our overall program.

3. What teacher has not discovered how _____ a yawn, sneeze, or cough can be in a classroom!

4. Modern technology has yet to produce an instrument or device that can match the consummate _____ sensitivity of a human finger.

5. None of the public buildings in the bombed city remained _____ after that most devastating air raid.

6. How can you describe something as _____ as a soul to one who has never before been exposed to the concept?

7. I am amazed that Alice, who is so blunt in talking to her friends, can show so much _____ when handling adults.

8. The speaker went off on a(n) _____ and never dealt directly with the topic under discussion.

Units 13-15

sed, sess, sid—to sit, settle

This root appears in **sedate** (page 102). The literal meaning is "settled," but the word now means "quiet or calm." Some other words based on the same root are listed below.

assess	**obsessed**	**sediment**	**subsidiary**
dissidence	**residual**	**subside**	**supersede**

From the list of words above, choose the one that corresponds to each of the brief definitions below. Write the word on the line at the right of the definition, and then in the illustrative phrase below the definition.

1. to displace in favor of another; replace; force out of use _____

   _____ all the other officials

2. excessively troubled or preoccupied by _____

   _____ by fear of illness

3. to grow less; become less active; to die down (*"to settle down"*) _____

   when the excitement _____

4. furnishing aid or support; of secondary importance; a thing or person that assists or supplements _____

   a(n) _____ stream

5. matter that settles to the bottom of a liquid; lees, dregs _____

   filtered out the _____

6. to estimate the value of; to fix an amount, tax; to determine the importance, value, or size of _____

   _____ each member a dollar

7. disagreement in opinion or belief; dissent   _____

     a meeting marred by noisy _____

8. remaining; left over   _____

     _____ money

From the list of words on page 137, choose the one that best completes each of the following sentences. Write the word in the space provided.

1. Will nuclear fission ever _____ fossil fuels as the major source of energy in the United States?

2. The elderly are often _____ by the fear of being robbed or injured by young hoodlums.

3. Party officials sought to quell the growing _____ in the ranks by ousting the leaders of the disgruntled faction.

4. How accurately can present-day diagnostic tests _____ the true potential of any teenager?

5. When the floodwaters finally retreated, residents returned to find their little village covered with a layer of muddy _____ .

6. Under the United States Constitution, state governments may exercise those _____ powers which are not assigned to the Federal government and not forbidden to the states.

7. Only when the master of ceremonies finally raised his hand did the giggling in the audience _____ .

8. The raw materials needed by that giant corporation are supplied mainly by its own _____ companies.

The following tabulation lists all the basic words taught in the various units of this workbook, as well as those introduced in the *Vocabulary of Vocabulary* and *Building with Word Roots* sections. The number following each entry indicates the page on which the word is first introduced. Exercise and review materials in which the word also appears are not cited.